JEREMY SIEPMANN

# Brahms

## EVERYMAN–EMI MUSIC COMPANIONS

GENERAL EDITOR MICHAEL ROSE

Copyright © David Campbell Publishers Ltd.
and EMI Records Ltd., 1997

Music compilation ℗ and © 1997 EMI Classics (USA)

Text copyright © Jeremy Siepmann, 1997

ISBN 1-85715-604-8

Published by David Campbell Publishers Ltd., 79 Berwick Street,
London W1V 3PF

Distributed by Random House (UK) Ltd., 20 Vauxhall Bridge Road,
London SW1V 2SA

A CIP catalogue reference for this book is available from the
British Library.

Front endpaper: Johann Strauss II conducting in heaven,
Brahms dancing with Hans von Bülow. Silhouette by Otto Böhler
(Lebrecht Collection).
Back endpaper: key to the above.
Frontispiece: Willy von Beckerath's most famous picture of
Brahms. Note the use of both feet on the pedals, the ubiquitous
cigar, and the bag of sweets in his pocket, ready for any child
he might encounter. Tempera painting, 1911, after a sketch from
the 1890s (Archiv für Kunst und Geschichte, Berlin/AKG London).

Design by Anikst Associates
Picture research by Josine Meijer
Typeset by AccComputing, Castle Cary, Somerset
Printed and bound in Germany by Mohndruck Graphische Betriebe
GmbH, Gütersloh

*Old Hamburg and the Petrikirche before the devastating fire of 1842. Lithograph by Peter Suhr.*

# Preface

All biographies are incomplete. The briefer they are, the more they must leave out. But a biography is more than a repository of facts. It is an exercise in portraiture. Its aim must be to render as truthful and vivid a picture of its subject as the limitations of its brief will allow. To that end, I have adopted a somewhat unusual approach here. The sequence of chapters is based on generic rather than strictly chronological principles, though the chapters themselves do follow a generally chronological line of development. Thus each chapter can be read as a self-contained entity in its own right, and in any order. And each affords at least a glimpse of the composer at several different stages of his life.

To compensate for any lack of continuity that this may produce, I have added a rather extended chronology of Brahms's life at the end of the book. Discussion of the music has been reserved, by and large, for the similarly organized Interludes, which again can be read selectively and in any order, though here the particular sequence is linked, albeit sometimes rather loosely, to the subject and content of the preceding chapter.

The selection of facts and themes for discussion has inevitably been a painful and frustrating procedure, nowhere more so than in the case of Brahms's triangular relationship to Robert and Clara Schumann. Clara still looms large, Robert, alas, less so. Another casualty of limited space is the very moving story of Brahms's relations with his parents, stepmother and stepbrother.

I have also (but only partly for reasons of space) kept 'interpretation' to a minimum, allowing the story to be told in large part by Brahms himself and those who knew him, and leaving readers to form their own impressions of a highly complex, frequently surprising and often endearing personality.

# CHAPTER 1

# Brahms and Childhood

*While the world still boasts people like Brahms, with the heart of a child and the character of a hero, I do not fear for humanity.*

Dr Richard Fellinger

*(left) Brahms's birthplace, no. 60 Speckstrasse, Hamburg – an apparently moribund tenement which stood the test of time until it was levelled by Allied bombing in the Second World War. The Brahmses' apartment was behind the double windows at the far left of the first floor.*

At home there was tranquillity, order, warmth and beauty. Outside, in the rat-infested dockland slums of Hamburg, was poverty, filth, disease and squalor. Brahms's childhood, indeed his life, was framed by such extremes. At one level, his story is a classic tale of rags-to-riches, except that he had no interest in riches and gave away, anonymously for the most part, vast quantities of the money that poured into his coffers as he reaped the benefits of his reputation as the greatest composer of his time.

Like many great artists he was compounded of paradox. To a degree and in ways beyond our telling, his creative fires were stoked by the continuous friction of apparent opposites. Cautious to a fault, he was possessed of a titanic self-confidence. A sense of destiny was with him long before Schumann hailed him as a musical Messiah, yet he was genuinely modest and disliked being made a fuss of. Tactless, lonely and curmudgeonly, especially in later life, he nevertheless attracted and reciprocated the devoted friendship of men and women alike, and was capable of the most unstinting generosity (it was largely he who put Dvořák on the international map). While idealizing femininity as a concept, he abhorred all forms of incipient

*Brahms's father in 1838.*

or outright feminism, and seemed at times to regard the generality of women with ill-disguised contempt. The struggle to integrate the masculine and feminine elements of his own personality fundamentally shaped the character of his art, nourishing an intimacy of musical expression comparable only with Schubert's. Nowhere is this more evident than in his many songs, whose particular conjunctions of notes and words served as a lifelong diary of the soul and repay the closest attention, both musical and biographical, with insights of extraordinary poignancy. As a composer he inflamed hordes of fanatical detractors, yet from his day to our own his music has retained its place at the centre of the Western musical tradition. Nor was his influence and importance confined to composition. As editor, arranger and conductor he was among the first great antiquarians, repeatedly bringing to public attention works by such then forgotten composers as Schütz and Palestrina. For all his conspicuous failings, and behind an incongruous exterior (at the height of his fame he looked a natural target for the Salvation Army), he was one of the noblest spirits of his own or any other age. But he was far from nobly born.

His father, Johann Jakob Brahms, the son of an innkeeper and grandson of a wheelwright, had demonstrated at an early age a passion for music which his parents did everything to discourage. With a stubbornness later passed on to his son, he ran away from home three times in search of tuition before his father finally relented and had him indentured, at the age of fourteen, to the local town musician. He now trained in earnest as an orchestral player, acquiring a creditable proficiency on all of the stringed instruments as well as the flute, the French horn and the bugle. On completion of his apprenticeship, he set off on foot, a double bass strapped on his back, to seek his fortune amidst the bright lights of Hamburg. Near penniless, and with no great talent or accomplishment to recommend him, he earned a pittance playing in dockside dives and lodged in a sequence of slum-dwellings before working his way through the ranks to become a horn player in the Hamburg militia and a member of a Palm Court-type sextet at the fashionable Alster Pavilion. Now twenty-four, easy-going, rather handsome, and blessed with a steady though very modest income, he took lodgings with two middle-aged sisters, whose genteel but impoverished family, in striking contrast to his own, could be traced back to the fourteenth century. Within a week of his arrival, he proposed to the younger, and on 9 June 1830, they were married. No one was more taken aback by this turn of events than the bride herself. Frail, lame and strikingly plain, Johanna Henrike Christiane Nissen, a seamstress by trade, was seventeen years her husband's senior. At forty-one, she had long accepted the role of spinster and was at a loss to explain her appeal to the young and personable musician. As she recalled many years later, in a letter to her famous son:

*Your Auntie and I grew up very simply. I was thirteen when I started going out to sew. In the evenings I came home at six o'clock, then I liked to give mother a hand, and sometimes I sewed until midnight. Six years I went on like that. Then I worked for ten years with very respectable employers as a general servant. Then again I went*

*Brahms's mother in later life – a force to be reckoned with, even without her teeth.*

*Sister Elise in 1860. Her frail health and propensity to migraines led to a semi-invalid existence.*

*out sewing ... Then Auntie married, and I lived with her, helping out in the family shop, and earning what I could by sewing. Father [Johann Jakob] took a room with us, and so we got acquainted. When he said he wanted me to become his wife, after only being with us for a week, I could hardly believe it, because our ages were so different.*

But he'd chosen well. There is no evidence to suggest that Christiane was ever less than a model wife. Intelligent, though not highly educated, warm-hearted and companionable, blessed with an equable temperament and a gift for impeccable but unobtrusive organization, she was devoted to her family and they to her.

Almost exactly nine months after their wedding, Christiane gave birth to their first child, a daughter, Elisabeth (later called Elise), born in February 1831. It had already become painfully apparent that Johann Jakob's meagre income was inadequate to his family's needs, and by the time their first son Johannes was born, on 7 May 1833, they were living in a cramped apartment in one of Hamburg's most notorious slums, the so-called Lane Quarter, known to the locals as 'Adulterer's Walk'. The building itself, for all its moribund appearance, stood essentially unchanged until 1943, when it was destroyed in an Allied bombing raid. In 1902, however, Florence May, a former pupil of Brahms, and his first English biographer, visited his birthplace and left us a description which perfectly complements the surviving photographs:

*The house and its surroundings testify only to the commonplace reality of a bare and repulsive poverty ... Each of its habitations is planned exactly as every other, excepting that those near the top are contracted by the sloping roof. Jakob and Johanna [Christiane] lived in the first-floor dwelling to the left on facing the house. On entering it, it is difficult to repress a shiver of bewilderment and dismay. The staircase door opens on to a diminutive space, half kitchen, half lobby, where some cooking may be done and a child's bed made up, and which has a second door leading to the living-room. This communicates with the sleeping-closet, which has its own window, but is so tiny it can scarcely be called a room. There is nothing else, neither corner nor cupboard. Where Jakob kept his instruments and how he managed to practise are mysteries which the ordinary mind cannot satisfactorily penetrate.*

*Brother Fritz ('the wrong Brahms') in 1870.*

Two years after the birth of Johannes, Christiane gave birth to their third and last child, Friedrich (or Fritz), whose misfortune it was to follow his brother into the musical profession, where he was known throughout Hamburg as 'the wrong Brahms'.

Whatever the physical and psychological hardships of his childhood, 'the right Brahms' was extraordinarily lucky in the forces that shaped his development, both human and artistic. Outside of school, and apart from his siblings, his first-hand experience of life was gained almost wholly in the company of adults. Unlike many exceptionally gifted children, he seems never to have been unduly penalized by his schoolmates for his apparently inborn sophistication and rampant curiosity, though possibly because he kept such things very close to his chest. As in his maturity, so in childhood, his inner life was a closely guarded secret. No great composer ever spoke more reluctantly of his creative impulses or took such pains to cover his traces. In his outward demeanour, however, he was not a particularly withdrawn, let alone a melancholy child. He was friendly, quiet and well-liked, though he seems never to have formed close friendships with his classmates.

His home life was happy, and made few concessions to the poverty which circumscribed it. His mother kept everything spotlessly clean, flowering plants adorned the rooms whenever funds allowed, caged birds filled the air with their song, and pride of place among the brightly coloured pictures on the walls went to a pastel portrait of Christiane as a young girl, proudly decked out in a pretty red dress with a tight bodice and short sleeves. Christiane herself maintained an outlook of continual optimism, buttressed by a simple but profound religious faith, and both parents shared a love of festive ritual which may have contributed to Brahms's later, unfashionable reverence for the clear-cut musical forms of earlier times. One sacrosanct family tradition, again when funds allowed, was the annual Christmas goose; another was the festooning of picture frames with garlands on family birthdays, followed in the evening by toasts drunk in Frau Brahms's celebrated egg-nog (comprising one bottle of rum, twelve eggs, four lemons and a pound and a half of sugar). Despite the scanty provisions with which she had to make do, Christiane was an exceptional cook, a fact attested to not only by Johannes but by such cosmopolitan luminaries as Joseph Joachim and Clara Schumann. It was generally agreed that her bilberry fritters were incomparable.

With her simple faith, strong character and steadfast generosity of spirit, it was Christiane more than her husband who provided the stability in the child Brahms's life. Ever on the lookout for advancement, both socially and professionally, Johann Jakob had an unsuccessful and moderately costly fling with the lottery, he unwisely persuaded Christiane to open a shop (the additional burden of work was more than she could cope with, and the venture soon folded, predictably at a loss) and later tried his hand at rearing chickens, pigeons and rabbits, again to no avail. It says something for the stability of their outwardly improbable union that she bore all these ill-fated adventures with equanimity and that the children, whatever their physical privations, grew up in an atmosphere of exceptional marital harmony. Brahms remained devoted to both parents throughout their lives and bitterly resented suggestions that he had been exploited as a child.

For all their hopes of improving circumstances, both parents agreed without demur that their first priority was to secure the best possible education for their children, or at least for their sons (the rights of women had scarcely been broached in mid-nineteenth-century Germany). Johannes successively attended two private schools, emerging from the latter at fifteen with a thoroughly respectable grounding in history, mathematics and literature, as well as a rudimentary reading knowledge of English and French. Strange to say, he proved singularly inept as a linguist and was never able to speak anything but his native German, despite a protracted love affair with Italy, which he visited many times. His half-hearted attempts to speak French, in which his accent was almost contrivedly dire, may reflect his mother's oft-expressed bitterness at Hamburg's treatment by Napoleon. Despite the assertions of many early biographers, Brahms's education was as good as could reasonably be expected. Indeed, his second school was widely known for its 'progressive' methods. In addition to a good reputation for its teaching of languages, both ancient and modern, it specialized in mathematics and natural history. And very exceptionally for a school of those times, it had a well-equipped gymnasium. Here, presumably, lie the roots of a charming reminiscence by Eugenie Schumann (fourth daughter of Robert and Clara):

*I see, as though it were in a picture, a group of children standing in the hall of our house in Düsseldorf. With amazement and admiration they are looking up at the banisters, on which a fair young man is performing the most daring gymnastics. He hoists himself from right to left and up and down; at last he raises himself firmly on his arms, his legs held high in the air, and a final leap lands him below in the midst of the admiring crowd of children. I and my elder brothers and sisters were the children; the young man was Johannes Brahms.*

It was also at school that Brahms made his first close acquaintance with the Bible, which he came later to know, despite his lapsed faith, with the thoroughness of a sound theologian.

*

It was fortunate that Johannes inherited his father's love of music, for he was destined from birth to enjoy all the privileges denied to Jakob by his own father.

Accordingly, he had lessons in violin and cello from the age of four, but the piano played no part in Jakob's plans. Entranced with the instrument from the first time he heard it, Johannes embarked on a campaign of attrition which is the earliest evidence we have of his exceptional determination and patience. Only after three years of Johannes's unceasing pleas did Jakob relent. There was no question of buying or housing a piano, but Jakob's choice of a teacher marked the first great turning point in his son's musical career.

Otto Friedrich Willibald Cossel, though himself of modest means, was no neighbourhood hack but a musician of incorruptible integrity and a teacher of genuine devotion. Unusually, in a time when the taste was for the light-hearted confectionery churned out by such fashionable note-spinners as Herz, Hünten and Kalkbrenner, Cossel not only gave Johannes a thorough grounding in piano technique but introduced him to the deeper reaches of the composer's art. It took him little time to realize the extraordinary gifts of his new pupil and within three years student was beginning to outstrip teacher. The boy's astonishing progress suffered a momentary setback when he was run over by a carriage in the street, one wheel passing over his chest, but such was his robust constitution that he returned to something like normality within a mere six weeks.

When Johannes was ten, his father, hoping to raise much-needed funds, arranged a concert at which Brahms appeared in a Mozart piano quartet and the Beethoven op. 16 Quintet for piano and wind, neither of them remotely student fodder. In the audience was a travelling impresario who offered Jakob unimaginable riches if he would emigrate to the United States and allow his son to tour as a child prodigy. Jakob, unsurprisingly, was overjoyed; Cossel was appalled: the *Wunderkind* trail, then as now, had been the graveyard of many precocious talents. To begin with, his protests fell on deaf ears. Faced with the promise of untold affluence after years of penury and hardship, Jakob could hardly be expected to welcome the suggestion that he throw the chance away. Cossel now played his trump card. If Jakob would agree to stay, Cossel would arrange for Johannes to study with one of the most distinguished and admired teachers in all Germany.

Eduard Marxsen, of nearby Altona, had been Cossel's own teacher and the two had remained good friends and mutually respectful colleagues. That Jakob not only accepted but welcomed the arrangement says much for his integrity and common sense. He was not, like the parents of all too many prodigies, a cynical fortune-hunter but, as Marxsen himself later described him, 'a thoroughly upright character, of limited intellect, perhaps, but of the greatest good nature'. Thus it was that in 1843 Marxsen became the third and last of Brahms's music teachers. And he was of excellent pedigree: in Vienna, he had studied composition with Mozart's friend and pupil Ignaz Seyfried (a friend, as well, of both Haydn and Beethoven), and his most important piano teacher, Carl Maria von Bocklet, had been a friend and early champion of Schubert's.

Unlike Cossel, who regarded Brahms's burgeoning interest in composition as a threat to his pianistic development, Marxsen actively encouraged it, giving him lessons in musical theory and in compositional techniques for which Brahms remained eternally grateful (throughout his career he paid heartfelt tribute to both teachers, and it was to Marxsen that he dedicated his great B flat major Piano Concerto in 1881). Long after Brahms left Hamburg, the two men continued to correspond, and to the end of Marxsen's life Brahms regularly submitted works to him for comment, corrections and advice. It was through Marxsen, too, that he acquired his early skill in counterpoint and his lifelong passion for the then unfashionable works of Bach and Beethoven.

Since neither space nor money allowed for a piano in the home, Brahms was forced to do his practising elsewhere, either at Cossel's house or in piano showrooms. This necessarily disjointed existence, combined with the rigours of school life, regular trips to Marxsen in Altona, and the responsibilities of teaching (at twelve, he was already giving piano lessons) now took its toll of his health and he began to suffer badly from migraine. He was soon to experience a further drain on his energies, however, and one which was to leave him emotionally scarred for life.

Although his musical education had incurred only incidental costs (Marxsen refused to take a fee), the family remained in poverty and from the age of thirteen Johannes was compelled to earn what he could playing popular dance music in the bars and 'stimulation saloons' (*Animierlokale*) of Hamburg's notorious St Pauli district. In these sordid, squalid dives, frequented by drunken sailors and the lowest class of prostitutes, the apple of his parents' and of Marxsen's eyes brought in a pittance to the family exchequer but was offered compensation by his employers in the form of free liquor ('as much as he can drink!'). Here, on a regular basis, Johannes, on the threshold of puberty, saw sex, avarice and lust at their most degraded and repulsive. He declined the proffered liquor, but distracted himself from the surrounding degradation by reading while he played: volumes of poetry by Eichendorff, Novalis, Hölderlin and Heine or the fantastic novels and stories of E. T. A. Hoffmann which he bought from the second-hand bookstalls lining the canal.

During this period, according to his friend Klaus Groth, Brahms suffered so badly from anaemia and an acute form of anxiety that 'he could only walk along an avenue by staggering from tree to tree, if he were not to fall'. While this smacks a little of adolescent histrionics, there can be no doubt that Brahms was under a dangerous strain, both physical and psychological. That he escaped a nervous breakdown is a tribute not only to his own inner strength and resilience but to all those concerned with his welfare.

Among these was one Adolf Giesemann, a gentleman farmer and frequenter of the Alster Pavilion who had struck up a friendly acquaintance with Jakob and who now proposed that Johannes should spend some weeks at the family home near Winsen an der Lühe, some fifteen miles out of Hamburg. Thus began the happiest period of Brahms's boyhood. He returned his hosts' hospitality by giving lessons to Giesemann's daughter Lieschen, a lively, happy child, one year Johannes's junior, who shared his love of music and of reading. It was his first experience of close friendship with a contemporary, as it was also his first acquaintance with the open countryside. From that summer of 1847 dates his lifelong love affair with nature. Rambling through forests and meadows, gathering wild flowers, swimming in the river, he was almost able to forget the debilitating squalor of his urban life.

In addition to teaching Lieschen, he contributed to the musical life of nearby Winsen, playing duets with the local bailiff, and conducting the Winsen Choral Society, for whom he even composed some part-songs. Home and lessons were not, however, entirely forgotten. He and Lieschen made several trips to Hamburg, travelling up-river by steamer. By the time of his return to school that autumn, his health was restored and he was scarcely to know a day's illness until the final months of his life, more than half a century later. Nor did he return to the *Animierlokale*, but made better money playing in respectable restaurants.

In the spring of 1848, a year of momentous change for Europe, Brahms left Hamburg for Winsen, temporarily, and school for good. Apart from his continuing studies with Marxsen, he was now on his own. But the story of Brahms and childhood was far from finished.

\*

The polarities of his boyhood persisted in his later life. As he idealized or demonized women, so did he come to idealize children. He loved them above all, in contrast to his generalized, suspicious view of adults, for their simplicity, innocence, and honour. The compulsive teasing which brought him both renown and notoriety amongst children themselves was often no more than an awkward expression of tenderness, but it could equally mask well-meant if misguided attempts at education. This was especially the case in more affluent families, when he suspected the children of being spoiled by their parents. 'Uncle Brahms', with his Santa Claus beard and pockets stuffed with sweets, was a popular figure in many families at home and abroad, but for the very young (as, it must be admitted, for many of their elders) he could be perplexing company. While few doubted the sincerity of his affection for children, there were occasions when he would abuse their trust, turning rapidly and unpredictably into a figure of fear rather than fun. As his friend and first great biographer Max Kalbeck recalled:

*He would take a little one on his knee with apparent friendliness, but scarcely was he seated there before Brahms would threaten to snip off his nose with a cigar-cutter. When he was reassured, and asked perhaps for a drink of water, the Master would pour it down the back of his neck inside his little dress. The small girls, on the other hand, always had their apron strings untied, however much they turned and twisted. Then, when they were all worked up with apprehension and fear, Brahms went away well pleased.*

Whether such things were a frequent occurrence, however, is open to doubt, though Kalbeck's children in particular seem to have come in for more than their share of light-hearted abuse. 'We always used to fear him,' the daughter remarked. 'His hands were so hard, and his "love-pats" used to hurt.' But as she also observed, they were children of the rich, at least in Brahms's eyes. From an old peasant woman in Ischl, where he spent many of his last summers, comes a very different picture:

*Although Master Brahms hated many kinds of sound, children never bothered him, no matter how much noise they made. Once he bought a lot of toys for them from a strolling gypsy-woman. Then he pretended to be very much excited and told our mother that the gypsy had forgotten the toys and that she should make the children run after her and give them back. But mother had happened to see Master Brahms pay for them, and was not taken in.*

From Ischl, too, he wrote to Clara Schumann:

*You ought to see me here in the role of the children's friend! There are no more lovable and agreeable folks and little folks anywhere than in this neighbourhood. I cannot go for a walk without my heart laughing; and when I caress a couple of these adorable children I feel as though I'd taken a long, cooling drink.*

The role was nothing new, as Clara had repeatedly observed in her own household.

Certain childhood enthusiasms remained with him for life, notably his near obsession with tin soldiers. In the warm, enveloping haven of his very humble home, he had never tired of setting them up, in endlessly varying permutations. A curious passion, on the face of it, for so sensitive and introspective a child, but the fascination was organizational not militaristic. For Brahms, it was a kind of visual, tangible counterpart to the invisible, unmaterial world of composition. A mixing and juxtaposing of colours and textures, a deploying of finite and clearly delineated forces in a theoretically infinite variety of combinations. Above all, perhaps, it arose from a deep-rooted need and love for order, but an order reflecting the organic unity and

*At Gmunden in 1895*
*with Olga von Miller*
*zu Aichholz and her*
*daughter. It would*
*appear that the latter*
*has been embarrassed*
*by some Brahmsian*
*witticism.*

flexibility of life itself. Most music is at one level or another an art of variation. In Brahms's music, the concept of developing variation within the confines of a logically constructed form is fundamental. To this extent, the difference between his soldiers and his symphonies is only slight, and his continuing enthusiasm for both is not so hard to understand. As he approached the age of thirty, he continued to marshal his metallic forces with undisguised delight, and decades later, near the very end of his life, he could be found lying on the floor assisting his landlady's children in the deployment of their own battalions. Nor did he outgrow the favourite books of his youth. Late in life he showed a friend his dog-eared copies of *Robinson Crusoe* and *Paul und Virginie*, confessing that they still captivated and thrilled him.

Other, more occasional pleasures likewise rekindled the child in him. When he was forty-three and adding the final touches to his long-awaited First Symphony, he joined his friend Georg Henschel for a nature crawl on the island of Rügen, in the Baltic. 'We lay in the grass and caught tiny frogs, then letting them jump from a stone down into the water. This pleased Brahms enormously, in particular when the sprightly little creatures, glad to be again in their element, hastily swam away, moving their hind leglets in accordance with all the laws of the swimmer's art. Then, when the little frog thought it had escaped, Brahms caught it gently again, and letting it go, he laughed with all his soul.' He derived a similar, infantile mirth from playing practical jokes on his friends. After his death, his housekeeper recalled the ridiculous delight he took in a trick rocking-chair: 'He often amused himself by making his visitors take this seat – especially handsome women. If the fair arrival perched gingerly on the front edge, she either fell on her knees or ignominiously plumped down upon the floor. If, on the other hand, she boldly sat well back, her feet suddenly flew up to an alarming height. In either case, Brahms would succumb to helpless laughter.' Another favourite amusement was to ambush his guests, 'cowering behind a fire-screen', as described by his friend Widmann, 'and then, at the right psychological moment, bursting forth with daemonic laughter like a mischievous hobgoblin'.

Throughout his life, Brahms was prone to the unbridled and unselfconscious enthusiasm of happy children everywhere, often deriving a keen pleasure from the most unlikely sources, as when he wrote to his publisher Simrock, 'Not for a long time have I had such a beautiful treat as at a fire in Schwerin recently. Standing near a hose, on the flat roof of the house adjoining, I looked right down upon it. It was extraordinary! If a house *must* burn, the very least one can do is to enjoy watching it!' It was not the first house he'd seen burned. Among the most vivid memories of his boyhood was the terrible Hamburg fire of 1842 which had raged for three days, levelling five thousand buildings and sparing the nine-year-old Brahms's home thanks only to a last-minute change in the wind. As sometimes happens, the fear and horror experienced at the time were resolved into a cathartic enthusiasm, and Brahms retained a weakness for incendiary delights to the end of his days, even in one instance allowing it to overcome his chronic reluctance to stay overnight at the homes of his friends. The occasion was the seventieth birthday party of his friend Hanslick.

*Customarily he excused himself from such hospitality on the specious ground that he did not possess a suitable coat. But this time he had been promised fireworks, which he adored. I watched him leaning over the balustrade; and as each rocket went up he gave a great 'Oh!', in which his whole stocky frame took part. He almost yodelled with joy at the spectacle.*

In other pleasures he took a more active role, joining in snowball fights with the schoolgirls of Krefeld or wrestling on the lawn with some of his friends' more obstreperous dogs. For all his undoubted melancholia, his loneliness, for all his occasional bitterness and his cyclical bouts of misanthropy, Brahms had a childlike genius for finding joy in simple things. His capacity for enthusiasm was unbounded, and he never lost it. It was the life-blood of his apparently limitless energy. As Florence May recalls, he was an indefatigable walker, and his love of nature was a continual source of spiritual renewal.

*It was his habit during the spring and summer to rise at four or five o'clock, and, after making himself a cup of coffee, to go into the woods to enjoy the delicious freshness of early morning and listen to the singing of the birds . . . 'I never feel it to be dull,' he said one day, in answer to some remark about the depressing effect of long-continued rain. 'My view is so fine. Even when it rains, I have only another kind of beauty.'*

Of this beauty Brahms speaks in a letter from the village of Tutzing, near Munich:

*We have just had the most gorgeous thunderstorm; the lake was almost black, but magnificently green along the shores; usually it is blue, though of a more beautiful and deeper hue than the sky. In the background there is a range of snow-covered mountains – one can never see enough of such things.*

In 1881, the year of his forty-eighth birthday, he wrote to Clara Schumann from Rome, in a characteristic transport of delight: 'Why do I not stay here until driven out by heat and insects? It is the most lovely spring imaginable; I enjoyed the first spring in Sicily, the second here, and in Vienna I shall have my third!' He rejoiced in the autumn, too, though it was spent in town. From Vienna in October, 'I eat midday and evening in the open air and the chestnuts above me are luxuriantly blooming for the second time.' But from Ischl, in the summertime, he reminds her

*With Johann Strauss, whom he greatly admired, at Bad Ischl in 1889.*

that his joys are not confined to Nature: 'It is wonderfully beautiful and pleasant here. And as I've often said before, I am made most happy by the charming people about me!' As they were often charmed by him – by his vitality and humour, and by his seemingly inexhaustible curiosity. As Widmann wrote in 1886:

*I have never seen anyone who took such fresh, genuine and lasting interest in the surroundings of life as Brahms, whether in objects of nature, art, or even industry. The smallest invention, the improvement of some article for household use, every trace, in short, of practical ingenuity gave him real pleasure. And nothing escaped his observation ... He hated bicycles because the flow of his ideas was so often disturbed by the noiseless rushing past, or the sudden signal, of these machines, and also because he thought the trampling movement of the rider ugly. He was, however, glad to live in the age of great inventions and could not sufficiently admire the electric light, Edison's phonographs, etc. He was equally interested in the animal world.*

And just as children can listen to the same story again and again without growing tired of it, so Brahms seemed to derive a curious comfort from repetition: 'I always had to tell him anew about the family customs of the bears in the Bern bear-pits before which we often stood together. Indeed, subjects of conversation seemed completely inexhaustible during his visits.'

Nor did it seem ever to occur to Brahms that his enthusiasms were not shared by all his friends. He was pushing thirty when he wrote to Clara Schumann:

*I often pass a shop in which I have discovered the most beautiful soldiers. Yesterday I went in to buy an acrobat for Felix [Clara's son], and at the same time to have a look at them ... At present I have the most fascinating battle-piece I ever saw, with a little tower as well. I am overjoyed with it. At Christmas I will set out all my troops so beautifully you will be delighted with them.*

And this from a man who had already composed the D minor Piano Concerto, the B flat String Sextet, the 'Handel' Variations and substantial chunks of the German Requiem!

# Brahms and Variation

The first well-documented Brahms work we hear of is the 'Fantasia upon a Favourite Waltz' which he played at his second solo outing in Hamburg at the age of sixteen. It was at the same time that he picked up extra money making arrangements and pot-pourris of popular music under the collective pseudonym of G. W. Marks (see p. 76). In all of these the principles of variation were paramount, and they seem early on to have become a part of his artistic bloodstream.

Indeed after the heroic triptych of sonatas completed in 1853,* and with the sole exception of the op. 10 Ballades, the second phase of Brahms's career as a piano composer was entirely concentrated on the art of variation – a process which was to dominate his music for the rest of his life, and in almost every branch of his output, culminating in the great passacaglia which concludes his Fourth Symphony.

Not surprisingly, his earliest work in the form is based on a theme of Schumann. Written in 1854, in the wake of Schumann's collapse, it shows most of the hallmarks of the great sets which follow it: a remarkable mastery of contrapuntal devices and imitative procedures, a highly disciplined organic development through a wide range of moods and textures, a brilliant command of a truly pianistic idiom, and an unobtrusive but ruthless subordination of bravura to purely musical ends.

Also characteristic is his unwillingness to repeat himself. His every essay in the

---

*For discussion of these, see p. 57.

form explores new challenges and different demands. The two sets which make up his op. 21 are as different from each other as from their predecessor, op. 9, and it's the first set, on a theme of his own, which claims the lion's share of our attention. Less varied in tone, and with no hint of bravura (but by no means easy to play), it largely eschews the contrapuntal preoccupations of op. 9 (although the fifth variation is a quietly taxing 'canon in contrary motion'), concentrating instead on harmonic and structural considerations. The theme alone is beautiful, moving, and unmistakably Brahmsian, conveying, like certain of the variations to follow, something of the elegiac mood of the slow movement of the D minor Concerto. Its unusual use of nine-bar phrases is typical of Brahms's lifelong fascination with metrical and rhythmic ambiguity (phrases of five, seven and nine bars being particularly favoured). The relative neglect of this profound and very beautiful work is hard to understand, though its predominantly slow-moving and contemplative nature may offer at least a partial explanation. The second (and markedly inferior) set, written in 1853 on the theme of a Hungarian song, gives us our first taste of that gypsyish strain which was to recur in many of Brahms's works throughout his career. Nothing here is more ear-catching than his metrical scheme, with its time signature of seven beats to the bar, in alternating groups of three and four beats respectively.

The most comprehensively satisfying, and the most popular, of Brahms's large-scale piano works is undoubtedly his op. 24. Completed in 1861, the Variations and Fugue on a Theme of Handel have been at the centre of the piano repertory ever since. Given the extraordinary variety of his invention and the width and depth of his emotional range, it seems scarcely credible that he preserves the original proportions and even the original key of the theme throughout (albeit with the odd excursion into minor). Only in the gigantic concluding fugue does he expand the scale, and here, from the very outset, we feel ourselves to be embarking on a great adventure. Such is the dramatic power and the unerring psychological pacing that one easily overlooks the contrapuntal ingenuity and masterly control which lie behind them.

As befits the man who provided their theme and inspiration, the Variations on a Theme of Paganini are of formidable difficulty. They come in two books but are frequently played together, and their alternative title, 'Studies for the Pianoforte', has given a wholly spurious justification to that great majority of pianists who play them as though they were little more than glorified exercises. For all their often fiendish difficulty these are primarily studies in sonority and characterization, as rich and sometimes as sensuous as anything by Liszt or Debussy.

All but three of Brahms's great variation sets (the slow movement of the B flat String Sextet and the Finales of the Fourth Symphony and the Clarinet Quintet) were originally conceived at and for the piano. The most famous and most popular of all, however, is Brahms's orchestral version of his own Variations on a Theme of Haydn, originally written for two pianos.* The great advantage of the orchestra over any number of pianos lies in its almost limitless possibilities for instrumental tone-painting. Brahms here relishes every opportunity to enrich the character and function of each new development, passing themes and motives from one instrument to another, from one section of the orchestra to another, and even dividing up single, long-spanned melodies between different instruments and sections. Analogies with football are not perhaps very poetic but in the most sophisticated possible manner Brahms is playing a similar game.

The principles and techniques of variation – not merely the additive, decorative variety but the organic, developing, transformational type – play an important role in most of Brahms's finest work. Listening attentively to the unfolding adventures of the great 'Handel' set makes an ideal gateway to this palace of riches. Rhythmic, melodic, harmonic, textural and temporal alterations, either in sequence or in combination, are essential features of the Brahmsian landscape.

---

*The theme is now known *not* to be by Haydn, and the work is commonly referred to today as Variations on the 'St Antoni' Chorale – this being a traditional tune set by Haydn (or possibly by Pleyel) in a little-known partita for woodwind.

# CHAPTER 2

# Brahms and Performance

*Johannes was blissful and played the last movement prestissimo from sheer delight
– I wish you could have seen his happiness.*

Clara Schumann on hearing Brahms play his D minor Concerto

*(left) Joachim in
Napoleonic pose, his
earnestness and self-
assurance clearly
evident.*

The year 1848 marked a watershed for Europe, and for Brahms. It was the year in
which he left school, at the age of fifteen, the year in which he gave his first solo
performances in public, in which he heard Beethoven's Violin Concerto played by
the astonishing seventeen-year-old Joseph Joachim, and the year in which he had his
first experience of opera (Mozart's *The Marriage of Figaro*, courtesy of his adoptive
'Uncle' Adolf Giesemann). It was the year in which Europe was riven by armed
revolutions in Vienna, in Paris, in Venice, in Rome and Berlin, in Prague and Buda-
pest. In time the political disturbances were to have a decisive effect on the shape
of Brahms's future; for the moment, however, Hamburg was little affected by the
surrounding tumult and his horizons were circumscribed by the same preoccupations facing most gifted but still unfledged young artists.

Five years had elapsed since Cossel and Marxsen had plucked him from the jaws
of American exploitation, during which time he had not once appeared in concert
in the role of solo pianist. He now found himself in an ambiguous position: at fifteen,
he had outgrown the role of child prodigy, though in appearance he could have
passed for ten, but was too young to rival the established virtuosos who dominated

Hamburg's pianistic fare. Solo recitals, of the kind we know today, were a still recent phenomenon. Liszt had inaugurated both the institution and its curious name, on 9 June 1840 at the Hanover Square Rooms in London. It was not, therefore, a sign of timidity or excessive caution that Brahms shared his first solo appearance as a pianist with two singers and a cellist. The concert took place before a small audience on 21 September and, according to the then still prevalent fashion, was largely given over to lightweight samples of saloniste confectionery by such now forgotten composers as Rosenhain, Döhler, Herz – and Marxsen, whose general high-mindedness didn't preclude the odd trifle. The daring inclusion of a Bach fugue, however, served fair notice that the fifteen-year-old Brahms was not just another would-be matinée idol but an artist of the most serious intent. The concert was accorded a polite but muted reception. As a potential career-launcher it was little better than a damp squib. Brahms, therefore, continued to provide innocuous light entertainment in restaurants and augmented his meagre earnings by taking on a few piano pupils whose parents were undeterred by his still soprano voice and childlike appearance. The following April he returned to the concert platform, again with a supporting cast, but he now began to bring out his big guns. The programme included Beethoven's great 'Waldstein' Sonata, a major work of virtuoso requirements and imposing musical substance, and still more significantly, the 'Fantasia upon a Favourite Waltz' by Brahms himself. Unfortunately we are left to guess at its character, dimensions and overall effect. If indeed he ever wrote it down (and it's highly possible that he didn't), he soon took care to eradicate all traces of it. Thus he began his composing career as he meant to continue it. It seems certain that no other great composer ever sacrificed more pages to the flames than Brahms. Not for him the creative trail left by Beethoven in his fascinating and illuminating sketchbooks. Nor even the painstakingly impenetrable crossings-out so often found in Chopin. So jealously did Brahms guard the secret workings of his mind that not so much as a watermark survives to facilitate the probings of the impertinent musicological researcher. This second 'solo' concert was better attended than the first, but was only politely received by the critics.

The career of concert pianist to which Brahms had so urgently aspired at the age of seven was off to a dispiriting start. But as the unveiling of his 'Fantasia' indicated, his priorities had shifted considerably in the meantime. The inherently inviolable privacy of composition had for some time been usurping the place of performance in his scale of priorities. Among its most practical advantages, of course, was the fact that it required no space. No matter how small or crowded the room, it could flourish relatively undisturbed – and Brahms's exceptional powers of concentration, already evident in early childhood, were proof against a sea of potential distractions. From a practical point of view, however, the piano remained his strongest suit.

\*

It was at around this time that Brahms's career and the political upheavals of Europe intersected. Among the hordes of refugees who flooded into Germany from the troubled Habsburg empire was Edu (or Eduard) Reményi, a gifted Hungarian violinist, five years Brahms's senior, who had made highly successful debuts in Paris, London and Pest (not yet united with Buda), before falling foul of the Austrian authorities and heading for the United States by way of Hamburg. While many of his fellow softcore revolutionaries did indeed cross the Atlantic, Reményi found much to his liking in Hamburg and decided to stay on, at least for a while. He arranged to give a number of recitals, engaging for one of them the young, safe Johannes Brahms (no fear of being upstaged by a mere boy, he may have reckoned). On meeting, the two musicians felt an instantaneous yet at the same time rather guarded rapport. The flamboyant, manipulative Reményi was deeply impressed by his newly acquired accompanist, while Brahms, for his part, was particularly entranced by the Hungarian's abandoned and seductive way with the heavily 'gypsyized' music of his homeland. It was the beginning of a love affair with 'Hungarian' styles which was to last him a lifetime and which bore its most famous though by no means its only fruit in the twenty-one Hungarian Dances.\* Their concert together proved to be the first of many, and after a considerable hiatus during which Reményi did indeed travel to America, they decided, in 1853, to undertake a tour of north German cities, playing a programme with which they had already enjoyed considerable success in Hamburg and Winsen: Beethoven's C minor Violin Sonata, the E major Concerto by Henri Vieuxtemps (Brahms standing in for the orchestra), Heinrich Ernst's then popular Elégie and a pot-pourri of Hungariana which reliably brought the house down. On 19 April (Brahms still some weeks shy of his twentieth birthday), the pair left Hamburg on foot and embarked on a journey whose consequences no one could have foreseen. When Brahms returned to Hamburg, alone, and after an absence that had stretched to seven months, his name was on the lips and his career in the minds of music-lovers throughout Europe. But this is to anticipate.

The tour began well, indeed spectacularly. On finding that the piano at their first port of call was mistuned, Brahms, quite unfazed, spontaneously transposed the entire programme up a semitone – effectively playing the C minor Sonata in C *sharp* minor, and entirely from memory. He hadn't bothered to pack any music. 'His memory', as Marxsen later observed, was 'so extraordinary that it never occurred

---

\*First written as piano duets, these 'exotic' pieces did more than any other branch of his output to make Brahms a genuinely popular composer.

to him to take music with him on his concert tours. Even as a young man of twenty, many of the works of Beethoven and Bach, besides a large number of modern concert pieces by Thalberg, Liszt, Mendelssohn and many others were indelibly impressed upon his mind.' On another occasion, with Joachim at Göttingen in 1868, he transposed Beethoven's 'Kreutzer' Sonata, for similar reasons, from A to A sharp.

At the time of this first tour, Brahms knew Joachim only from afar. Hearing him in the Beethoven Concerto at Hamburg in 1848 had been one of the greatest artistic experiences of his life. Although only two years Brahms's senior, Joachim, Hung-arian-born and a mere twenty-two years of age, was internationally renowned, not as a dazzling prodigy but as one of the towering figures of his day: a conductor and composer of distinction, and one of the very few violinists of any age whose interpretations of the great masterworks of the repertoire – most notably the Bach Chaconne and the Beethoven Concerto – were regarded as sovereign. Reményi had known him in Paris, where they had been fellow students, and now proposed in his own interest to renew their acquaintance, calling at Hanover, where Joachim was in charge of music at the royal court. Joachim received the pair at his home, and while he was characteristically gracious to his flashy former associate, it was the quiet Brahms who attracted his immediate interest. At length, Brahms was per-suaded to play some of his own music to Joachim, including movements from the first two Piano Sonatas and the now famous 'Liebestreu' – the first of Brahms's songs to find a permanent place at the centre of the vocal repertoire. Joachim was transfixed:

*Never in the whole of my artistic career have I been overcome by a more joyful aston-ishment than when my fellow countryman's shy, fair-haired accompanist played, with a noble uplifted expression, music whose astounding originality and power no one would have suspected. It affected me like a revelation when I then heard the song 'O versenk' dein Leid' for the first time. And his piano playing! So tender, so imaginative, so free and so full of fire that it held me absolutely spellbound.*

The disparity between the vainglorious Reményi and the taciturn genius at his elbow was immeasurable and Joachim perceived at once that their association was unlikely to last. Finding a suitably discreet moment, he invited Brahms to join him at Göt-tingen in the summer should the tour with Reményi for any reason come to grief. In the meantime, he arranged for the pair to perform for the king, but prior to the appointed hour the Hanoverian police had got wind of Reményi's unsavoury polit-ical reputation and had sent the duo packing.

Armed by Joachim with a letter of introduction to Liszt, the travellers now headed for Weimar, where the great Hungarian expatriate held court as the uncrowned king of the German avant-garde. Sumptuously ensconced at the palace of his cigar-smoking, Polish-born mistress, Princess Carolyne von Sayn-Wittgenstein, Liszt had renounced the concert life after establishing himself as the greatest pianist who ever lived, and now devoted himself with extraordinary energy to composing, teaching, and occasional conducting, as well as championing with unexampled generosity the music of other like-minded composers. Among the many musicians who found themselves impelled towards Liszt and Weimar were such disparate figures as Berlioz, Verdi, Borodin, Smetana, Grieg, Schumann, and most importantly of all, Wagner.* But while these great figures came and went, there was always a hard core of adoring acolytes who surrounded the master like a living halo and hung upon his every word.

All this was too much for the boy from Adulterer's Walk. Overcome by the opulence of his surroundings and discomfited by the pervasive atmosphere of hero worship, he withdrew within himself and could barely be prevailed upon to speak a single word. Liszt, affable and godly as ever, expressed a keen interest in Brahms's compositions. As their composer could not be persuaded to play them, Liszt himself sat down at the piano and read them off at sight from manuscript – note-perfect, alive to every nuance, and with staggering virtuosity. Nor did Liszt confine himself to playing but kept up a running commentary on the music as it sprang to life beneath his fingers, congratulating the composer here, offering suggestions there. As he did so, it became increasingly clear to Brahms (as it probably also did to Liszt) that the two of them inhabited different worlds and breathed a different musical air. The impression was cemented when Liszt afforded the young Brahms a privilege for which many musicians would figuratively have sacrificed a limb. Putting the young man's manuscripts to one side, he proceeded to play the whole of his own Sonata in B minor, then just completed and now regarded by most musicians as his greatest work. And here we come to the hoariest chestnut in the whole of Brahms's biography.

The story goes (and there are several versions, differing only in details) that Brahms repaid his host's generosity and responded to his creative genius by nodding off to sleep. On reaching the end of his great work, Liszt is reported to have cast one look at his slumbering guest and departed from the room in silence. Despite its treatment as gospel by many biographers, however, there are reasons to doubt the story. Liszt himself is not known ever to have mentioned the incident. On the

*No important musician recognized Wagner's stature sooner than Liszt, or did more to champion his cause. And his services to Wagner were not confined to the merely musical. When Wagner was outlawed throughout Germany for his part in the Dresden uprising of 1849, it was Liszt who sheltered him in Weimar. It was Liszt who arranged his escape route to Switzerland, and Liszt, among many others, who gave him large sums of money whenever he needed it.

other hand, Brahms never troubled to deny it, but that was his lifelong if somewhat enigmatic policy. As he said in another context, 'Even if a newspaper were to print today that I had murdered my father, I wouldn't bother to reply.' The main source for the story is Liszt's American pupil William Mason. But though Mason was undoubtedly present at the occasion he was unable actually to see Brahms and relied for his information on the anecdotal evidence of Reményi, a notoriously unsafe witness who by the time of his interview with Mason had seriously fallen out with Brahms. And even if one discounts the extenuating circumstance of Brahms's physical and emotional fatigue at the time, is it likely that a young virtuoso would be anything but riveted by Liszt's pianism alone? As Brahms himself later said to Max Kalbeck, 'Whoever has not heard Liszt cannot even speak of piano playing. He comes first and then for a long space there is no one else. His playing is unique, incomparable and inimitable.'

Whether the disputed incident actually occurred is almost beside the point. The truth is that Brahms felt wholly out of sympathy not only with Liszt's music but with his artistic aims, a fact which was later to tempt him into one of the most egregious and self-defeating blunders in the history of musical politics. Of this and related subjects, more anon. Suffice it to say for the moment that the gulf separating Brahms and Liszt was essentially unbridgeable – a fact which may be gauged by the latter's reaction, many years later, to Brahms's B flat Piano Concerto, a copy of which had been sent him by the composer himself.

*Honoured Master,*
*I beg you to forgive my delay in thanking you for so kindly sending me your concerto. Frankly speaking, at first reading this work seemed to me a little grey in tone; I have, however, gradually come to understand it. It possesses the pregnant character of a distinguished work of art, in which thought and feeling move in noble harmony.*
*With sincerest esteem, most devotedly,*
*F. Liszt*

The civility of Liszt's tone here does little to conceal the deep-rooted incompatibility of the two composers, but neither does it give any hint of the passionate factionalism which divided the European musical scene for many years. The combative nature of the rift is well illustrated by Hans von Bülow's ringing declaration to the piano-maker Bechstein, 'We Weimarites are going to win, you'll see; we shall rule and our opponents will dissolve in gall and be poured away down the closet of the past! And our art – the true, the noble, the high – will thrive greatly; and Liszt will be hailed as the founder of interpretative art, with all its implications, and the initiator of a new era.' In the meantime, Brahms, from his place in the opposing camp, reports: 'The Weimarites continue their uproar. My fingers often itch to do battle, to begin to write anti-Liszt!' The itch was placated, with lamentable results (see p. 140), but when it came to writing 'anti-Liszt', the golden palm must be awarded to Joachim, who in 1857 gratuitously wrote to the composer one of the most extraordinary letters in the history of musical correspondence:

*I can remain silent no longer on a subject which, I confess to you, your manly spirit had the right to demand to know long before. Your music is entirely antagonistic to me, it contradicts everything with which the spirits of our great ones have nourished my mind from earliest youth. If it were thinkable that I could ever be deprived of, that I should ever have to renounce all that I have learned to love and honour in their creations, all that I feel music to be, your strains would not fill one corner of the vast waste of nothingness.* Take that, sir!

Perhaps inevitably, the young Brahms's obvious lack of enthusiasm for the entire Weimar scene brought about the sundering of his partnership with Reményi, who was hoping to make professional capital out of his acquaintance with Liszt. Nor was he disappointed. The Master of Weimar, always a soft touch when it came to Hungarians of gypsyish persuasion, became one of Reményi's warmest champions. In any case, Brahms's charms were wearing thin for Reményi, who was growing tired of being upstaged by his accompanist. The moment Joachim had anticipated prior to their departure from Göttingen was now at hand. Brahms bade a courteous farewell to Liszt, who conspicuously harboured no ill feelings, and headed for Göttingen and the future.

*

In Joachim, Brahms found not only an artist of incomparably greater distinction than any he had yet encountered, but a truly kindred spirit. And Joachim, whose knowledge of society and of the world at large dwarfed Brahms's own, reciprocated. As each seems instinctively to have recognized, their meeting marked a turning point for both. Unfortunately, Brahms's letters to his family at this time have not survived (probably at the wish of their writer) but in Christiane's replies one can easily read between the lines.

*Your letter surprised and moved us so much that we could hardly read it, and when we came to the end, we said: happy Johannes, and we his happy parents. Surely, yes, this exquisite feeling, not for all the treasures of earth would we miss it. Now, Johannes dear, your life really begins. Now you will reap what you have sown with toil and diligence here. Your great hour has come. You must thank Divine Providence which has sent an angel to lead you out of the darkness into the world where there are human beings who appreciate your worth and the value of what you have learned. How much we should love to be with you a few hours, to see your happy face, and tell each other how happy we are. Alas, it is impossible. We will pray to God for your health, which, however, you must not overtax, and you must not stay up too late at night!*

From the moment of their introduction, Joachim and Brahms had met as friends. Neither was ever to experience a closer sense of kinship. And though their friendship was later to be clouded, as sooner or later all Brahms's friendships were, they held each other, unceasingly, in the highest esteem to the end of their days. Brahms, who had never intended to stay so long away from home, remained with Joachim for much of the summer. Nor, for all the love he bore his family, was he in any hurry to return to Hamburg. In the tradition of mothers since time immemorial, Frau Brahms fretted anxiously and hungered for news.

*You have not written plainly enough about your circumstances. For example, you need no money. Even if you have free lodgings, food and drink, you must still have clean linen, your boots will wear out, and, after all, how can you live away from home without money? If you have to get every little thing from Joachim, you will be under too great an obligation to the gentleman. You had better write to Herr Marxsen. He can advise you in everything. But you must write the exact truth, otherwise the same thing will happen as with Reményi. You understand people too little and trust them too much.*

In the case of Joachim, she needn't have worried. No man ever had a more generous or honourable friend. With her mention of money, however, she touched a nerve. Brahms, for all the euphoria of these heady days, was in an awkward position. The rupture with Reményi had left him with no visible source of income, yet he was unwilling to go home empty-handed. As he put it to Joachim at the time, 'I cannot consider returning to Hamburg with nothing to show ... I must at least have two or three compositions in print, so that I can cheerfully look my parents in the face.' Joachim was unconcerned. He had his own thoughts about that. In the meantime, he wrote to Brahms's parents:

*Göttingen, 25 July 1853*

*Please allow me, although I am unknown to you, to write and tell you how infinitely blessed I feel in the companionship of your Johannes; for who better than his parents can know the joy which their son can give. Your Johannes has stimulated my work as an artist to an extent beyond my hopes. To strive with him for a mutual goal is a fresh spur for me on the thorny path we musicians have to tread through life. His purity, his independence, young though he is, and the singular wealth of his heart and intellect find sympathetic utterance in his music, just as his whole nature will bring joy to all who come into spiritual contact with him. How splendid it will be when his artistic powers are revealed in a work accessible to all! And with his ardent desire for perfection, nothing else is possible. You will understand my wish to have him near me as long as his presence does not interfere with his duty to himself. I believe, moreover, that Johannes too must find it pleasant to live undisturbed in quiet Göttingen, where he is sure of finding, in Musikdirektor Wehner and myself, two men who are glad to follow his idiosyncrasies in life and art. How glad I should be if I could ever render my friend Johannes a real service, for it goes without saying that my friendship is always at his disposal. I can only hope that our new bond will find the blessing of your approval,*

*Truly yours,*

*Joseph Joachim*

The effect on Brahms's parents of this letter from one of the greatest and most famous musicians in the world may easily be guessed.

A concert with Joachim brought in enough money to see him through the next few weeks at least, and in August Brahms set off for western Germany to widen his musical acquaintanceship and in the process to fulfil a long-cherished dream. In September he wrote to his friends in Winsen:

*I have passed a most heavenly summer, such as I have never known before. After spending some gloriously inspiring weeks with Joachim at Göttingen, I have now been rambling about for five weeks, according to my heart's desire, among the hills and valleys of the Rhine. I hope to be able to pass this winter at Hanover in order to be near Joachim, who is equally noble as man and artist.*

Back in Hamburg, Christiane clucked with characteristic maternal concern,

*It is a lovely trip you are making, but surely sometimes very dangerous. I do beg you, over such steep rocks! How easily you could fall there! I tremble when I think of it. And your chest is strong of course, but one can overdo a thing with too much climbing. Nestler's daughter, a woman of twenty-five, also made a pleasure trip into mountainous country and soon after she came back she died of a haemorrhage. Therefore, Johannes dear, please take care of yourself, and for heaven's sake don't go out in a thunderstorm. Malwine Erk was killed in Heligoland by lightning. But for today, enough of all these terrors. I can no longer think of them.*

Brahms himself, while heeding his mother's advice, had his mind on other things.

*Brahms in his early
20s – the time of his
acrobatics on the
Schumanns'
banisters.*

In Bonn, the birthplace of his greatest hero, Beethoven, he made a useful contact
in the person of the violinist and conductor J. W. Wasielewski, through whom he
made several valuable friends. And in every home he visited, his unremitting hard
work with Cossel and Marxsen paid rich dividends. Even those few listeners who
may have been resistant to his music were powerfully affected by his playing.

*

Unlike that of Liszt and Chopin, Brahms's prowess as a pianist has tended to get
lost in the shuffle. Yet it was primarily as a performer that he earned most of his
early keep, and though he let his technique slip in later years, his playing, like his
music, was profoundly individual. That it provoked equally individual responses
in his listeners must surely be attributable, in part, to the attitudes which lay behind

it. In his playing, as in his music (and later in his manners too), he was amongst the least ingratiating men who ever lived. This is not to deny his undoubted charm and humour, or to discount the love and exceptional devotion he inspired in his many lifelong friends, but while the approval of others was as gratifying to him as to anyone else, he seldom courted it.

As Joachim put it, within a year of their first meeting:

*He will not make the smallest sacrifice of his inclinations – he will not play in public because of his contempt for the public, and because it irks him – although he plays divinely. I have never heard piano playing (except perhaps Liszt's) which gave me so much satisfaction – so light and clear, so cold and indifferent to passion.*

So cold and indifferent to passion? As we shall have further cause to reflect, Joachim's psychological insights were not always a match for his musical genius.

Between 1854 and 1860 – that is to say for most of his twenties – Brahms the composer fell strangely silent. With the sole exception of the four Ballades of 1856, he published nothing for six years. During this outwardly fallow spell he relied for his livelihood on teaching and performing, without evincing great enthusiasm for either. As a performer he was generally ambivalent, and to certain of his colleagues, Clara Schumann among them, his plaintive attitude to concert tours was understandably offensive:

*You regard them merely as a means of making money. I do not! I feel I have a mission to reproduce beautiful works, and especially Robert's, so long as I have the strength to do it. The practice of my art is an important part of my ego. It is the very breath of my nostrils.*

The implication here, whatever his attitude to touring in particular, is unfair to Brahms. His nostrils, too, could quiver with evangelical zeal, and he was tireless in championing the music he loved best. 'How Brahms loved the great masters!' wrote Julius Schmidt, a cellist at the court of Detmold during Brahms's time there in the 1850s. 'And how he played Haydn and Mozart! With what beauty of interpretation and delicacy of tone! And his transposing! . . . His score-reading too was extraordinary. Bach, Handel, Haydn, Mozart, all seemed to flow naturally under his fingers, and each point to come out, as it were, of itself.' The degree and passion of Brahms's humility in the face of the great masters was not lost on his more perceptive critics. After a concert in Leipzig on 10 January 1855 at which he played the Beethoven G major Concerto and a group of solo works by Schumann, the critic of the *Signale* summed up the general reaction when he wrote, 'Many artists could certainly have displayed more technical brilliancy, but few have the capacity for bringing out so convincingly the intentions of the composer, or following as

Brahms does the flight of Beethoven's genius and disclosing its full splendour.'

At a later concert, the Viennese critic Selmar Bagge was likewise in no doubt about the quality of Brahms's pianism: 'We have to bestow the very highest praise not only on the enormous technical acquirement, but also on a performance instinct with musical genius, and a treatment of the instrument quite as fascinating as it was original.' Even Brahms was pleased. As he wrote to his parents the next day, 'I was really very happy yesterday. My concert went quite excellently, much better than I had hoped. Every number was greatly applauded. I think that there was real enthusiasm in the room [!]. I played as freely as though I were sitting at home with friends; and I must say that one is certainly influenced quite differently by the public here than by ours.' Of the range and deployment of Brahms's tonal palette there can be no doubt. Schumann, too, was struck by its sheer individuality. 'His playing,' he wrote, 'belongs essentially to his music. I do not remember ever having heard such original tone effects before.'

Not all his colleagues were so enthusiastic. The great Russian pianist Anton Rubinstein heard Brahms in 1855, and wrote dismissively to Liszt, 'I hardly know how to describe the impression he made on me; he is not polished enough for the drawing-room, not fiery enough for the concert hall, not simple enough for the country, and not cosmopolitan enough for the town. I have no faith in this kind of nature.'

Nothing in music is more subjective than the evaluation of performance, especially by musicians themselves, but accounts of Brahms's playing, as of his conducting in later life, are more than usually contradictory. As indicated earlier, he was distinctly inconsistent in his attitudes, and this was true throughout his life. In 1863, we find him writing to Clara, 'What pleases me most is that I really have the gifts of the virtuoso. I am entirely dependent upon the kind of piano I have. If it is good I play with the greatest calm and ease. The bigger the pieces, the better I play.' Yet a few months later he complains to Joachim, 'I can no longer feel myself at ease in a virtuoso's skin.'

Brahms's ambivalence towards performance was essentially that of a composer: it was something that got in the way. As he remarked in a letter to his parents in 1862, 'I could very well give more concerts but I have no wish to do so, for it takes up so much time that I can do nothing else.' There was a compromise, of course, and he took it: he continued to give concerts, but gave up regular practising. In the succeeding four years, his concerts went from strength to strength, his public and the critics none the wiser. Typical of his reviews was the following from the *Wiener Presse* in March 1867:

*At last a pianist who entirely takes hold of one! One only needs to hear his first few chords to be convinced that Herr Brahms is a player of quite extraordinary stamp.*

*He was received by the entire very numerous public with applause such as is seldom heard in Vienna concert rooms.*

Nor was his programme standard fare, consisting of an extended Fantasia by Bach, Beethoven's Fantasy, op. 77, his own E flat minor Scherzo, both books of his ferociously taxing Variations on a Theme of Paganini, Schumann's *Etudes symphoniques* and, finally, his own piano arrangement of the Fugue from Beethoven's C major String Quartet, op. 59 no. 3. Less than a month later, having in the meantime given several recitals in the Austrian provinces, he was back with another programme, this one featuring Bach's F major Toccata, Beethoven's Sonata no. 30 in E major, op. 109, his own Variations and Fugue on a Theme of Handel, op. 24, the Schumann Fantasia in C, op. 17, short pieces by Scarlatti and Schubert, an arrangement from Schubert's great Octet in F, plus a sprinkling of vocal items with Brahms as accompanist. We know that Brahms took no music with him on any of his tours. Can it really be that he delivered himself of programmes like these without practising either? From Joachim, writing to his wife at around this time, comes the only hint we have: 'Brahms says he is going to *practise*, believe it who may! He makes a new resolution to do so every day.' Ten years on, he was at least practising on the day of the performance. In February 1876 he and Georg Henschel both appeared as soloists at a concert in Koblenz. 'When I arrived at the hall on the day of the concert,' wrote Henschel,

*I found Brahms quite alone, seated at the piano and working away for all he was worth on Beethoven's Choral Fantasia and Schumann's Concerto. He was quite red in the face, and, interrupting himself on seeing me stand beside him, said with that childlike, confiding expresssion in his eyes: 'Really this is too bad. These people here tonight expect to hear something especially good, and here I am likely to give them nothing but a hoggish mess. I assure you, I could play today, with the greatest ease, far more difficult things, with wider stretches for the fingers, my own concerto for example, but these simple diatonic runs are exasperating. I keep saying to myself, "Johannes, pull yourself together – do play decently", but no use; it's really horrid.'*

On the contrary. It went brilliantly.

   If Brahms was inconsistent in performance, he was no more so than many other great artists. True inspiration cannot be put on tap, and truly great playing cannot occur without it. But the Muse will not be bullied. To hear Brahms at his greatest could require patience. When the young English pianist Florence May arrived in Germany in the 1870s to study with Clara Schumann she struck lucky sooner than most.

*Frau Schumann wished me to hear him play, but it was no easy matter to do so, as*

*he was extremely dependent on his mood, and not only disliked to be pressed to perform, but was unable to do justice either to himself or to the composer when not in the right humour. The first time, indeed, that I heard him, I was utterly disappointed ... Frau Schumann answered that I had not yet really heard him; that he had not wished to play, but had yielded to over-persuasion, and that I must wait for a better opportunity.*

This arose, as it happens, the next evening. As Florence May wrote to her parents:

*It was an entirely different thing from the day before. Two pieces were by a composer whose name I can't remember, but then he played a wild piece by Scarlatti. He really did give it as though he were inspired; it was so mad and wild, and so beautiful. Afterwards he did a little thing of Gluck's. I can only hope I shall hear him often if he plays as he did last night. It was like nothing I have ever heard before, and I would never have believed the piano capable of it.*

She did hear him often, and the composer he played most frequently and with the most evident sense of rapture was Bach. As her recollections constitute the most detailed evidence we have of Brahms's interpretations at the piano, they are quoted here at length.

*It was my happiness to hear many of the forty-eight preludes and fugues [Bach's Well-tempered Clavier], and his playing of them impressed me with such force and vividness that I can hear it in memory still. His interpretation of Bach was always unconventional and quite unfettered by traditional theory, and he certainly did not share the opinion, which has had many distinguished adherents, that Bach's music should be played in a simply flowing style. In the movements of the suites he liked a great variety of tone and touch, as well as a certain elasticity of tempo. His playing of many of the preludes and fugues was a revelation of exquisite poems, and he performed them not only with graduated shadings but with marked contrasts of tonal effects. Each note of Bach's passages and figures, in the hands of Brahms, combined to form melody which was instinct with feeling. It might be deep pathos, or light-hearted playfulness and jollity; impulsive energy, or soft and tender grace; but sentiment (as distinct from sentimentality) was always there; monotony never ... He particularly loved Bach's suspensions. 'It is here that it must sound,' he would say, pointing to the tied note, and insisting, whilst not allowing me to force the preparation, that the latter should be so struck as to give the fullest possible effect to the dissonance ... The same kind of remarks may be applied to his conception of Mozart. He taught me that the music of this great master should not be performed with mere grace and lightness, but that these effects should be contrasted with the expression of sustained feeling and with the use of the deep legato touch ... Brahms, in fact, recognized no such thing as what is sometimes called 'neat playing' of the compositions either of Bach, Scarlatti or Mozart. However, neatness and equality of finger were imperatively demanded by him, and in their utmost nicety and perfection, but always as a preparation, not as an end ... Brahms's playing at this period of his life was, indeed, stimulating to an extraordinary degree, and so apart as to be quite unforgettable. It was not the playing of a virtuoso, though he had a large amount of virtuosity (to put it moderately) at his command. He never aimed at mere effect, but seemed to plunge into the innermost meaning of whatever music he happened to be interpreting, exhibiting all its details and expressing its very depths ... As a performer, he was acutely, though silently, sensitive to the susceptibility or non-susceptibility of his audience.*

An interesting adjunct to May's remarks on Brahms's 'elasticity of tempo' occurs in Clara Schumann's diary, where she confesses that she 'cannot quite get used to the constant change of tempo in his works; and besides, he plays them so entirely according to his own fancy that today, for example, although I was reading the music, I could not follow him, and it was very difficult for his fellow players to keep their places'. This sounds both improbable and exaggerated, but as it comes from one of the greatest and most sophisticated performers in pianistic history it can hardly be ignored.

A similar distinction can't, of course, be claimed for Clara's daughter Eugenie, but her own remarks on Brahms's playing, particularly of his own music, also merit our attention.

*Interesting as his playing was, there was always something of a fight, a touch of animosity about it. I do not believe that Brahms looked upon the piano as a dear, trusted friend, as my mother did, but rather that he considered it a necessary evil with which one had to put up as best one could. It was not always perfectly enjoyable to hear Brahms play his own compositions, but it was always highly interesting. Marie [Eugenie's sister] once characterized his rendering of the B flat Concerto as 'a spirited sketch'. He played the themes with great emphasis and curiously free rhythms; merely outlining everything in the nature of accompanying sections, so that one had the impression of strong light and shade. When he came to the passionate parts, it was as though a tempest were tossing clouds, scattering them in magnificent fury. He then made one feel the limits which the instrument imposed upon him.*

And he certainly grew more careless as he grew older. But Clara's diary entry of 29 December 1881, when Brahms was still under fifty, seems more bad-tempered than just: 'Brahms plays more and more abominably – it is now nothing but thump, bang and scrabble.'

*Brahms on the rostrum, c. 1890. These famous drawings by Willy von Beckerath speak volumes for Brahms's conducting style.*

More interesting, and surely more reliable, are the reflections of the Austrian critic and Brahms biographer Richard Specht:

*I heard Brahms play only in the last decade of his life, both in the concert room and in the circle of his friends, and I heard him in a great variety of works. Each time, and each time in a different way, he made an indelible impression on me. He had by then long given up regular practice, although his technique was still equal to any difficulty encountered in his own works. But it was not dazzling; he would often play as if to himself and was then capable of muttering the choicest things into his beard. His touch was sometimes hard when he played loudly, but in delicate passages, magically fragrant, songful and rich in light and shade. It is certain that I never heard anyone else play Brahms's piano music as its creator himself played it. The whole man was in the performance, and the whole work too: you possessed it from that moment – irrevocably. His playing, for all its reticence, was filled with song. There was in it a searching, a gliding of light and flitting of shadows, a flaring and burning out, a restrained masculine feeling and a self-forgetful, romantic passion such as I have never experienced elsewhere.*

In considering Brahms as a performer we are not, of course, dealing only with a pianist. From the age of fourteen, when he first took on the Winsen Choral Society (see p. 10), he appeared with increasing regularity as a conductor, both choral and

symphonic, and often both – as at the world première of the German Requiem in 1868, when he was thirty-five. In the audience was Clara Schumann.

*As I saw Johannes standing there, baton in hand, I could not help thinking of my dear Robert's prophecy, 'Let him but once grasp the magic wand and work with orchestras and choirs,' which is fulfilled today. The baton really was a magic wand and its spell was upon all present, even upon his bitterest enemies. It was a joy such as I have not felt for a long time. After the performance there was a supper in the Rathskeller, at which everyone was jubilant – it was like a music festival. Reinthaler made a speech about Johannes which so moved me that (unfortunately!!!) I burst into tears. I thought of Robert, and what joy it would have been to him if he could have lived to see it.*

Over the next five years, Brahms's stature on the rostrum increased with every concert. In 1873, his friend Billroth noted, 'Brahms is now extremely active as a conductor. He has achieved incomparably fine performances, and receives the fullest recognition from all who take art seriously.' Of these, none was more serious than the eminent conductor Hermann Levi, one of several great musicians who demonstrated, in the teeth of fashion, that it was possible to harbour equal enthusiasm for both Brahms and Wagner, and who freely acknowledged his debt to each. In the case of Brahms, he wrote to Clara Schumann in 1864: 'I believe that my close contact with Johannes has had a deep and lasting influence on my entire character, such as I cannot remember having experienced at any other stage of my musical life. In him I have seen the image of a pure artist and man; and that is saying much nowadays.' Nor was his admiration confined to Brahms the composer. Five years on, he wrote to Brahms himself, after a concert: 'I have now seen – and with unprejudiced eyes – *that you have a gift for conducting such as no other man possesses*' [italics mine]. Given the source of this accolade, one ought perhaps to take with a grain of salt Richard Specht's flat-footed pronouncement: 'That Brahms himself was entirely devoid of the manual skill of conducting, that his wrist lacked the required elasticity, is scarcely to be questioned.' How so 'required'? If Brahms was 'entirely devoid' of skill, he must, then, have drawn on some other resource. That he got exceptional results is indeed 'scarcely to be questioned'. A typical concert in Vienna in 1873, as we learn from Billroth, 'awakened such a storm of applause that one almost feared the house would fall in. The old king of Hanover was almost beside himself with musical intoxication. And one does truly become quite drunk with the beautiful quality of sound this choir produces under Brahms.'

Despite his great successes elsewhere, the one position Brahms coveted above all others ironically eluded him – namely the conductorship of the Hamburg Philharmonic. When the position fell vacant in 1862, he was passed over in favour of his far less experienced friend, the singer Julius Stockhausen, whom he himself had introduced into Hamburg musical society. From Vienna, the twenty-nine-year-old Brahms wrote disconsolately to Clara Schumann:

*This is a much sadder business for me than you think, or can perhaps understand. As I am altogether rather an old-fashioned person, so I am in this, that I am not a cosmopolitan but love my native town as a mother ... And now this hostile friend comes and ousts me ... perhaps forever. How rare it is for one of us to find a permanent niche, and how glad I should have been to find mine in my native town! Happy as I am here, with so much beauty to rejoice in, I nevertheless feel, and shall always feel, that I am a stranger and can find no peace ... As a general rule, what our fellow citizens like best is to acquire the things that make life worth living, and one dreads solitude. Work, in active association with others, with live social intercourse and family happiness, who is so little human that he does not long for these things?*

Thunderstruck, for his part, at this blatant miscarriage of justice, Joachim wrote in protest to Avé-Lallement, one of Brahms's Hamburg 'friends' who had great influence with the Philharmonic Society.

*How anyone, having to choose the director of a concert institution between him [Stockhausen] and Johannes can decide for the former, I, with my limited musical understanding, cannot apprehend! I regard Johannes so highly. With his gifts and his will there is nothing he cannot undertake and overcome! You know that as well as I. If the committee and orchestra had met him with confidence and affection instead of with doubt and airs of protection,* it would have removed the asperity

*In 1869, with his friend Julius Stockhausen, the singer and conductor whose appointment as music director of the Hamburg Philharmonic in preference to Brahms outraged Joachim and deeply saddened the composer.*

from his nature. *Whereas it must constantly make him more bitter, with his touching, almost childlike patriotism for Hamburg, to see himself put second ... I should like to give the committee a moral cudgelling (and a bodily one too!). This slight to Johannes will not be forgotten in the history of art.*

Nor has it been. Indeed it was compounded five years later when Stockhausen resigned and Brahms was once more rejected, this time in favour of another Julius, von Bernuth of Leipzig. On the occasion of the orchestra's fiftieth anniversary,

Brahms, in an unguarded access of self-pity, blamed the Society for more than just his professional disappointment. 'Twice,' he snarled to his friend Klaus Groth, 'twice have they filled the vacant position with a stranger. Twice have they passed me over. Had I been elected at the right time I might still have become a respectable citizen; I could have married and lived like other men. Now I am a vagabond.'

Levi had tried to soothe him. Expressing again his own unbounded enthusiasm for Brahms's conducting, he then quite rightly pointed out, 'You are not the man to contend successfully with the thousand-and-one petty vexations which are inevitably connected with any official position.' Nor, if he *had* married, is it likely that he would have coped any better with the vexations of matrimony. But that's another story (see Chapter 6).

# Brahms and the Concerto

As a medium, the concerto stands as the apex of the performer's art. Brahms appeared repeatedly as soloist in concertos by other composers, and it was wholly characteristic that he interpreted his role as 'first among equals' rather than gladiatorial hero. By the standards of the time his performances were often regarded as unduly self-effacing and austere.

Brahms wrote four concertos of his own, all of them great, all of them big, all of them strikingly different from their siblings. And they frame his entire output as an orchestral composer, the D minor Concerto (for piano) opening the sequence, the Double Concerto (for cello and violin) closing it. The story of the youthful D minor Concerto [CD1] is dealt with elsewhere (see pp. 139 and 150), but its initial, catastrophic reception may have had something to do with the fact that more than twenty years elapsed before Brahms returned to the medium. This he did in 1878, when he was forty-five and world-famous.

Because of its almost symphonic emphasis on the orchestra and the tremendous demands it makes on the soloist, the D major Violin Concerto was famously described by Hans von Bülow as a concerto not for but *against* the violin. The great violinist Bronislaw Huberman came closer to the truth, however, when commenting that 'this concerto is neither *against* the violin, nor *for* violin *with* orchestra; it is a concerto *for* violin *against* orchestra – and the violin wins!' Certainly the violin had never been asked to combat the orchestra as it does here. For all the beauty in the

work, there are moments in the first movement when the style of the violin writing is deliberately *un*beautiful. Indeed this is perhaps the first violin concerto, and certainly the first *great* one, in which the composer demands downright violence from the soloist. When it came to the expression of human emotion, Brahms, like Beethoven before him, was an uncompromising realist. And the rapturous, sometimes heartbreakingly poignant love music which permeates so much of his output is all the more affecting because of the pain and strife which are also there.

Brahms originally planned to give the work four movements, setting the seal on his conception of it as a kind of symphony with violin obbligato. In the end he scrapped that idea and inserted what he described as 'a feeble Adagio' – a typical Brahmsian joke – which ranks with the most expressive and beautifully crafted things he ever wrote. If it's true, as some claim, that concerto finales are generally

*Hungarian dancers in Carl Bantzer's oil painting* Schwälmer Tanz, *1898.*

disappointing, this one is a dazzling exception, not only bringing the work to a glorious conclusion, but qualifying on its own as one of the most jubilantly self-confident of all Brahms's 'Hungarian Dances'.

With the B flat Piano Concerto of 1881, Brahms moved still closer to the idea of the concerto as symphony-with-soloist. This time he does have four movements, the 'extra' being the Scherzo which comes second in the sequence, followed by the slow movement and Finale. The work's difficulties are colossal but like the Violin Concerto it steadfastly abjures bravura display. Its epic, organic integrity, too, is truly symphonic. From the very opening, leisurely horn call and its responsive pick-up by the piano, it's clear that we're in for a big, expansive work. In fact from the first bar of the piano's answer – even the first beat of it – we can hear the potential for a musical acorn to become a mighty oak. The little triplet figure in the horn call is immediately taken up and expanded by the piano, where it is extended to every beat. Two bars into the piece, and *development* is already taking place. That innocuous little group of three notes in the opening line serves almost as a motto for the whole movement. The powerful, driving Scherzo is the most straightforward movement from an interpretative point of view, but its difficulties are fearsome. Here too Brahms engages in some of his most memorable rhythmic manipulations.

Like the first movement, the love-drenched Andante begins with the distinctive tone of a solo instrument – not the piano, as one might expect, but the cello. Indeed the cello seems for a long while to have supplanted the piano as the soloist. This whole opening section, indeed the whole movement, is among the most inspired and lovely things Brahms ever wrote. If the element of tone colour plays a large part in the first movement, which it assuredly does, there are parts of the slow movement where it seems almost to be the principal agent of expression.

The Finale finds Brahms at his sunniest and most carefree. Bar the odd exuberant outburst, everything is light and airy, even a little flirtatious at times; it's a movement which sounds (or should sound) effortless but which conceals some of the most formidable challenges in the pianist's repertoire.

The Double Concerto for violin and cello, the first ever conceived for this combination, dates from 1887. It was Brahms's orchestral swan-song , and it served, at least partially, to heal a rift with Joachim that six years earlier had seemed to put an end to their friendship (see p. 132). Even today, after more than a century of championing by many of the world's greatest musicians, this is the least popular of Brahms's concertos. Certainly it requires concentrated listening if it is to yield up its greatest treasures, but its occasional austerity and tightly-knit structure are more than matched by its rapturous outpourings and the sometimes almost erotic intertwinings and dialogues of the soloists. Considering the nature and range of the two instruments, their characterization as male (cello) and female (violin) is

perhaps inevitable, though none the worse for that, and Brahms's powers of transformational variation were never more naturally deployed than here. The middle
movement, based on two of his loveliest and most expansive themes, is meltingly
tender and the high-spirited Finale, like that of the Violin Concerto, is in the great
tradition of his popular Hungarian Dances.

# CHAPTER 3

# Brahms as Teacher

*My joy in learning is partly that it enables me to teach.*

Seneca, *Letters to Lucilius*

Although he took pupils from an early age, Brahms never regarded himself as a teacher. He never held, nor sought, a position at any institution, nor had he himself ever attended one. Widely cultured and formidably well-read, he was to a very large extent self-taught. As he told a new acquaintance in his twentieth year, 'I spend all my money on books; books are my greatest pleasure. I have read as much as I possibly could since I was quite little, and have made my way without guidance from the worst to the best.' Unlike the more flamboyant romantics, who wore their culture like a brace of medals, he never flexed his erudition. Indeed he would often conceal it, as Eduard Hanslick recalled:

*It never occurred to him to flaunt his wide reading (the absolute opposite of Liszt, who constantly tosses around Dante, Shakespeare, Goethe, Michelangelo, and Albrecht Dürer in his musical essays, along with Plato, Spinoza, Kant, and Hegel, of whom he himself has scarcely read a single chapter). Often one would only discover years later, after some cue gave him the necessary impetus, how deeply versed Brahms was in literary matters. Perfectly obnoxious, in his eyes, were those newest critics who quote Schopenhauer and Nietzsche the minute they take up a new opera or symphony. How intimately Brahms knew our classical literature, how deeply he absorbed the masterworks. His literary sympathies, I must confess, were not always entirely comprehensible to me, for example the fact that he could read Jean Paul over and over again, right into his old age. The same was true of the comic novels of Swift and Fielding, these in German translations. He had no talent for foreign languages and never learned enough French for even the most minimal household use.*

Like many people of exceptional ability and unbounded curiosity, Brahms was blessed with an extraordinary memory, and equally remarkable powers of comprehension. Never 'the merely well-informed man' cited by Alfred North Whitehead as 'the most useless bore on God's earth', he was a thinker, a natural born intellectual whose learning, from impoverished childhood to his dying day, was never tainted by snobbery. Like Beethoven, who once claimed to value friends 'only in so far as they are useful to me', so Brahms regarded education, and particularly in his youth he seized with relish every opportunity to widen and deepen his own.

In February 1856, when he was twenty-three, he gleefully put a proposition to Joachim: 'Let each of us send the other, once every fortnight, some contrapuntal exercises to be returned a week later with the other's criticisms together with some work of his own; and let us so continue for a long time, until both of us have become quite adept.' But sensing that his friend might show less zeal than himself, he laid down conditions: 'I would like to lay down a few rules which I consider useful. Every Sunday some work must go either back or forth … And whoever misses the day, i.e. sends nothing, will be fined one thaler, with which the other will buy himself some books.' In the event it was Brahms's library, not Joachim's, that grew fat on the proceeds. Books to Brahms were more than objects; they were friends, with the incidental virtue that they couldn't answer back. When urging his father to visit him in later years, he offered his library as inducement: 'You can often take your afternoon nap in the company of my books.'

Brahms's pupils in his mature years were few, and not of the front rank, but they received his undivided and discriminating attention. As with any great teacher, his approach was in every case tailored specifically, and perceptively, to the needs and personality of the pupil at hand. One was Eugenie Schumann, who had the inestimable benefit of studying with both Brahms and her mother, and her comparisons make for fascinating reading, though non-musicians may find part of it a little technical. 'Brahms,' she wrote in later years, 'united in himself each and every quality that might be supposed to exist in an absolutely ideal teacher of the piano, without having a single modifying drawback. I do not wish to rhapsodize; he would have been the first to object to this …' But she can't help herself:

*He was strict and absolute; he was gentle and patient and encouraging; he was not only clear, he was light itself; he knew exhaustively, and could teach, and did teach, by the shortest possible methods, every detail of technical study; he was unwearied in his efforts to make his pupil grasp the full musical meaning of whatever work might be in hand. He was even punctual! He gradually put me through an entire course of technical training, showing me how I should best work, for the attainment of my end, at scales, arpeggi, trills, double notes, and octaves. He had thought about such training and about technique in general much more than my mother, who had surmounted all technical difficulties at an age when one is not yet conscious of them. He also showed me just how to work: To begin with, he made me practise to him during a good part of my lessons, whilst he sat watching my fingers; telling me what was wrong in my way of moving them, indicating, by a movement of his own hand, a better position for mine, absorbing himelf entirely, for the time being, in the object of helping me. He also gave special attention to the training of my thumb, which, as many will remember, was given a very prominent part in his own playing. When the thumb had to begin a passage, he flung it on to the key with the other fingers clenched. As he kept his wrist loose at the same time, the tone remained full and round even in a* fortissimo. *He was never irritable, never indifferent, but invariably helped, stimulated and encouraged. At all times he adapted his teaching to my capabilities and the stage of my progress in a quite wonderful way.*

*Brahms, as well as my mother, was of the opinion that technique, more especially fingering, must be learnt through exercises, so that in the study of pieces attention could be focused solely on the spirit of the music.*

Where technical work was concerned, Brahms particularly admired Clementi's *Gradus ad Parnassum,* and assigned a great many of these still valuable studies, recommending her to begin with easy ones, but to play them as fast as possible. Many years later, he was to publish his own book of fifty-one Exercises, most of them taxing, all of them useful and some of them downright beautiful. They make an excellent preparation for his virtuosic Variations and Fugue on a Theme of Handel, op. 24, and still more so for the formidably difficult Variations on a Theme of Paganini, op. 35. Like most great composers, Brahms valued technique only as a means to artistic ends, and he was equally assiduous in his attention to interpretation. In the study of Bach's works, in particular,

*Brahms laid the greatest stress on rhythm, and gave numerous directions which, like seeds, took root and continued their growth throughout my musical life. They greatly increased my perception of the subtleties of rhythmic movement. He made it one of the principal rules that in constantly recurring figures the accents should always be the same, and that they should be stressed not so much by strong attack as by greater pressure on the accentuated and more lightness on the non-accentuated notes. The melodic notes of figures he made me play legatissimo; the harmonic, however, e.g.*

*the notes of broken chords, quite lightly. He never wrote purely rhythmic accents in above the notes, as he held them to be an integral part of the figure; but accents specially intended, or not self-evident, he marked, and pencilled in phrasing with slurs.*

Unsurprisingly to anyone familiar with his works, Brahms gave meticulous attention to syncopations. These he insisted had to be given their full value, and where they produced dissonances with the other parts he made his pupil listen to the rhythmic displacement in relation to each of the dissonant notes. 'He made the suspensions equally interesting,' Eugenie continues,

*I could never play them emphatically enough to please him. Of all the works I studied with him, I enjoyed the French Suites most. It was pure joy to work at them in this way, and he made me see things which I had hitherto passed by without noticing, and of which I never again lost sight. In any work of Bach, Brahms would occasionally permit an emphatic lifting of the notes (portamento), but never a staccato. 'You must not play Bach staccato,' he said to me. 'But Mamma sometimes uses a staccato in Bach,' I demurred. He then replied, 'Your mother's youth goes back to a time when it was the fashion to use staccatos in Bach, and she has retained them in a few cases.'*

Interestingly, Brahms offered comparatively little guidance to the expressive characterization of the music, confining himself for the most part to explanations of rhythm and simple but far-reaching rules for nuances. 'If I might venture upon comparison between my mother's teaching and his,' Eugenie concludes, 'I would say that my mother primarily stimulated imagination and feeling, and Brahms the intellect. To have been influenced by both was perhaps the most perfect teaching imaginable.'

*

Another of Brahms's sometime piano pupils has left an equally interesting but touchingly different account of her lessons with him. Florence May, a pianist with professional aspirations, was officially a pupil of Clara Schumann, but went to Brahms at her suggestion: 'He would be able to help you immensely with your technique. He has made a special study of it, and can do anything he likes with his fingers on the piano.'

She did as bidden, as did Brahms (indeed he rarely accepted a pupil except on Clara's recommendation). Any trepidation she may have felt soon vanished. She found his manner 'absolutely simple and unaffected', and his approach unique. '"How can I most quickly improve?" I asked him one day. "You must walk con-

stantly in the forest," he answered; and he meant what he said to be taken literally.'
Her letters home have a freshness and immediacy worth any number of posthumous
recollections.

*My lessons with Brahms are too delightful; not only the lessons themselves, but he
makes me feel I must practise all day and night . . . He is so patient, and takes such
pains. I can't understand his giving lessons, and yet he is never angry at any sort of
foolishness, but only says 'Ah! that is so difficult!' As for an hour's lesson, that is
nothing. He systematically arranges for an hour and a half. I absolutely revel in my
lessons. He never expects too much, but is always satisfied if one is really trying.*

He paid exhaustive attention to fingering, encouraging her to rely on all fingers
as equally as possible, and demonstrating the uses of fingering for purely musical
purposes. As with Eugenie Schumann, he tended to devote a great part of each
lesson to Bach, in this case to the preludes and fugues of the *Well-tempered Clavier*
or the English Suites (substantially more challenging than their 'French' counter-
parts). Again he was meticulously methodical but never rigid, gradually increasing
the amount and scope of her work as her abilities developed, and elucidating to a
greater extent than in the case of Eugenie Schumann the spirit and expressive subtleties of the music studied.

*His phrasing, as he taught it to me, was of the broadest, whilst he was rigorous in
exacting attention to the smallest details. These he sometimes treated as a delicate
embroidery that filled up and decorated the broad outline of the phrase, with the large
sweep of which nothing was ever allowed to interfere . . . In spite of his extraordinary
conscientiousness about detail, Brahms was entirely free from pedantry.*

If his piano pupils were few, his composition students were scarcer still. As he
grew older and more celebrated he became increasingly hard to approach and was
apt to send potential students packing unless they bore some testimonial from a
colleague whose judgement he respected. And even that was no guarantee. One
hapless pilgrim was the young Sibelius, who arrived at Brahms's door in the early
1890s with a letter of introduction from Ferruccio Busoni. His foot never crossed the
threshold. Others, more successful, lived to regret it. Hugo Wolf gained admission in
the early 1880s. As Brahms recalled some years later,

*The compositions he brought me did not amount to much. I went through everything
with him in great detail and called his attention to a number of things. There was
a certain amount of talent there, but he took things far too lightly. I told him quite
earnestly where the fault lay and referred him to Nottebohm for lessons. That was
too much for him; he left and never came back. And now he spits venom and gall.*

And continued to do so. Brahms made no bitterer foe.

To others, Dvořák above all, he could hardly have been more generous. But though he retained his admiration for Dvořák's gifts, he was not above the occasional, kindly knuckle-rapping, as when he thanked Dvořák for the dedication to him of a string quartet:

*Today I will just say that being occupied with your works affords me the greatest pleasure. I would give a great deal for an opportunity to discuss them with you in detail. You do write a bit hastily. If, however, you will fill in the missing sharps, flats and naturals, you will perhaps also take a second look at the notes themselves and at the part-writing. Please forgive me; it is very presumptuous to express such wishes towards a man like you. I will very gratefully accept the works as they stand and would consider a dedication of your quartet a signal honour.*

Many composers benefited from Brahms's advice. Only one, however, succeeded in becoming his pupil, in any formal sense, and this thanks largely to a request from Brahms's old teacher in Hamburg, Eduard Marxsen. Gustav Jenner was an intelligent if not exceptionally gifted musician from Kiel in north Germany, and his reminiscences offer interesting insights into the relative priorities which Brahms gave to piano playing and composition (and, it must be said, to female and male pupils). The two men had first met in Leipzig, towards the end of 1887, where Jenner's impressions were entirely consistent with those of Eugenie Schumann and Florence May.

Arriving from Berlin, late at night, Jenner checked in at the hotel where Brahms himself was staying.

*I will never forget the feeling that came over me as I noticed on the guest list 'Johannes Brahms, Vienna'.\* He had already gone to bed. Through an odd coincidence I was given a room directly adjacent to his, and as I entered, the sound of heavy snoring proclaimed the great man's presence. I undressed and lay down with a strange feeling of mingled awe, pride and anxiety ... When I came down next morning, Brahms had already breakfasted. He was smoking with evident relish and reading the newspaper. I was somewhat taken aback when I first saw him, for I had pictured him in my mind's eye as tall, and so could hardly grasp the fact that this diminutive, plump gentleman was actually Brahms. He received me with pleasant, simple kindness, intimated that he knew why I had come, and took great pains to help me over my*

---

*Brahms became a frequent temporary resident in Vienna during the 1860s and made the city his permanent home in 1869 (see p. 142).

*Vienna's Elisabeth Bridge, which Brahms must have crossed many times on his indefatigable walks. Coloured lithograph by Carl Waage after a drawing by Rudolf von Alt, 1860.*

*first embarrassment and shyness by every now and then putting to me some short, direct question, so that I was soon convinced of his good nature and felt unlimited confidence in him. He also made sure that I could thoroughly enjoy the wealth of beautiful new experiences that were there for me to enjoy in those unforgettable days. Once, during a walk, he put his arm in mine familiarly, remarking that he couldn't see well, which was perfectly true, and said, 'If you have brought along something nice to show me, then you may just leave it in my room.'*

Jenner obliged, and Brahms asked him to call at his room at seven the next morning to discuss his compositions.

*I presented myself punctually at the appointed time and found him at breakfast, fresh, rosy and the very picture of geniality. I had brought a trio for piano and strings, a chorus with orchestral accompaniment, unaccompanied choruses for women's voices, and songs; and found that he had made himself acquainted with each of them down to the smallest detail, and, indeed, later he never looked through work with me which he had not thoroughly examined beforehand.*

On 13 February 1888, Jenner arrived in Vienna to begin his formal studies, and again found Brahms the very image of avuncular solicitude. That day he dined with Brahms at the Red Hedgehog (Zum roten Igel) and afterwards they went to find a suitable lodging, giving preference to the older houses. In the course of their search, Brahms took every opportunity of acquainting Jenner with what he regarded as the truly sacred places of the city.

*Before one house it was 'This is the Auge Gottes', before another 'Look! Figaro was written there!' At length a suitable room was found near his own dwelling. 'This young man likes music,' said Brahms to the landlady. 'Will he be able to hear a little piano playing or singing here sometimes?' This she could not offer. 'Never mind, it does not matter.' Then he gave me one of his coffee-machines, along with plates, cups, forks, knives and spoons, so that I was comfortably settled the first day. The use of his library was at my disposal; his purse also. I could have as much money as I needed from him, but I was never obliged to take any, and never did so.*

On the morning of his first lesson, Jenner approached Brahms's lodgings with the keenest anticipation. But the teacher portrayed by Eugenie Schumann and Florence May, let alone the genial benefactor of those Leipzig days, was nowhere to be found. 'The memory of that first hour,' Jenner wrote later, 'will be with me till the day I die.' It was bitter:

*On the same day on which he had so nicely encouraged me to send off my works, he requested that I once again bring the Lieder I had shown him in Leipzig, so that he might discuss them with me more thoroughly. During the lesson he sat always at the piano, my work lay on the music stand, and I sat next to him. Yet never was a note struck on the piano, except when he wanted to demonstrate bad notes, or other transgressions in the composition, directly through their ugly effect. With one single exception, where Rottenberg and I played, in Ischl, four-handed variations of mine for him at his behest, I have never been allowed to perform my compositions for him at the piano. Because Brahms had judged the Lieder in Leipzig with relative mildness, I had hoped to hear kind words. But now, he abruptly changed his tone. He took up one song after another, showed me mercilessly, with severe figures of speech, how bad these Lieder were, and criticized my poor pampered babies so thoroughly, that not one good measure remained in them, and tears came to my eyes. And that was only the introduction. I was to feel his pedagogical rod of correction with yet more humiliation. He stood up and got some loose, yellowed pages. They were the manu-script of those songs by Robert Schumann, that Brahms himself had published some-what later, in a supplementary volume of Schumann's works. Then he seated himself again at the piano, and played and sang for me, especially that moving song 'To Anna', whose melody Schumann employed in the F minor Sonata, with such passion-ate devotion, that he could not hold back the tears of inspiration which came easily to him. 'Yes,' he said as he arose, 'Schumann wrote that, when he was eighteen years old; one must have talent, everything else gets you nowhere.' Then, as if the humili-ation had not yet reached full measure, he gave me back the so badly rumpled, and so quickly withered bouquet of my songs, that had seemed so graceful to me, and whose intoxicating fragrance I had so often ardently inhaled, and dismissed me with the ironic words: 'So, young man, do not amuse yourself further in this way!', a figure of speech much beloved by Brahms that I have often had to swallow from him. It was as if I had fallen from the clouds. The gravity of the situation could not have been brought home to me in a more harsh or heart-wrenching way. Just previously, he had called my works talented, and had done everything to raise my self-esteem. Why, then, had he called me back to Vienna, only to say to me, that I was without talent? It was necessary, in the time to follow, that I keep this clearly before my eyes, if I didn't want to give myself over to despair.*

In the entire course of their lessons, Jenner claimed, he never once heard an encour-aging word from Brahms, let alone praise for his work. Nor did Brahms's outward manner towards him ever change. Not, at least, in lessons. Elsewhere it could be different.

*If we were alone, he sometimes remained, as before, the old, dear, fatherly friend to me, yet in a larger group I soon learned to keep quiet, for I could be certain, that upon my first ever-so-harmlessly uttered word, he would bring me up short with an infinitely disdainful, 'You are indeed still very young', or 'That is indeed not so important'. I will not deny, that there were times of total dejection for me, yes, even of despair, when I believed that I would have to succumb. Fully a year later Brahms said to me casually, 'You will never hear a word of praise from me. If you cannot endure that, then that something, which you have, is worthy only of ruin.' These words were, for me, a deliverance. Why Brahms employed this strict and harsh style of educating me, whether he had found something frivolous, presumptuous, or even arrogant in my person, I do not know. It is certain that he practised his maxim, uttered countless times: 'One must not coddle the youngsters.' It may well be that he thought of his own youth, how he had victoriously fought many a hard battle on the way to his salvation: 'It's not likely, that anyone has had it as hard as I,' he said to me once, as I sat alone with him in the Igel on the evening of his birthday; and then*

*he told me sad things, that were to an extent known to me, from Klaus Groth's accounts. 'If my father still lived today,' said Brahms, 'and I were by chance to play the first chair second violin in some orchestra, at least then I could say to him, that I had become something.' He could speak thus, in justified pride: for everything that he was, he had done for himself.*

From time to time, Brahms thawed a little, expressing his satisfaction not in words but by gesture, as when, immediately following a lesson, he would show his pupil some of the great treasures in his priceless collection of manuscripts, or sit down and play to him a sequence of pieces by such then arcane composers as Domenico Scarlatti and C. P. E. Bach. Or he might read aloud some of the letters he continually received from ineptly disguised autograph hunters (a breed that enjoyed his unmitigated scorn).

*Exterior of Brahms's favourite haunt in Vienna, the Red Hedgehog. Whenever possible, Brahms preferred to sit outside. Aquarelle by Johann Wilhelm Frey, 1890.*

*Sometimes, too, he showed me gifts from unknown admirers, and asked me to keep them. Occasionally, on a beautiful spring morn, he was ready to give away everything that lay about in his dwelling. Only with books was he very particular. But once, as he returned to me a song cycle setting of Rückert's poems, he bestowed upon me a volume of Rückert's poetry, that he loved very much. The book came with a dedication and his signature. The former he scratched out with a knife, but let the name stand, and said only, 'Well, just a bit deeper.' Also, I soon noticed, that when passages were silently passed over, or works went entirely without comment, that these were the least objectionable. Most likely I heard nothing about their value, and it was not to be ruled out, that they were entirely insignificant. For only in a roundabout way would I occasionally hear, namely from Rottenberg, whether the content of my works had interested him. Respecting myself, it was for him entirely and solely a question of the degree of perfection.*

*

Brahms's educational endeavours were not restricted to his private pupils. Being almost entirely self-taught, he never equated education with institutions, but seized the potential of almost every circumstance to broaden and deepen the range of his own mind and those of his associates. To none of his performing activities did he bring a more burning, messianic zeal than to his work as a choral conductor. Unlike his orchestral concerts, where he was dealing with hardened professionals, his choral work brought him into regular contact with amateur musicians, many of them women, hungering for knowledge and spiritual enrichment. Brahms was only too happy to oblige. In bringing to their notice, and that of the wider musical public, many long-forgotten treasures of the Renaissance and baroque eras, he rendered a service to Hamburg and Vienna whose enlightening and enlivening effects long outlived him. Before his seraphic antiquarian initiatives, the masterpieces of Byrd, Willaert, Palestrina, Cavalli, Gabrieli, Schütz, Vivaldi, Handel, like most of the works of Bach, were unknown to most musicians, let alone the public. In the 1860s and 1870s, Brahms stood in the vanguard of musicological scholarship. At the time of his death, his private library of books and scores exceeded two thousand volumes.

The first of the several choruses Brahms conducted was the Hamburg Ladies' Choir, founded by him in 1859 when he was twenty-six but looked more like nineteen. Two years later, Clara Schumann paid him a visit, and was enchanted by what she found.

*I spent the time very pleasantly. We had a great deal of music together, and on Sunday, a party of us including some of the [choral] Society, went for a delightful*

*expedition in the steamer to Blankensee. When we got there, we sought out the most
beautiful trees in the garden and sang under them, Johannes sitting on a branch and
conducting.*

This was the relaxed, generous, extending Brahms who thanked one choir, after a
performance of his motet *O Heiland, reiss die Himmel auf,* saying, 'I didn't *compose*
it as beautiful as that!'

Brahms's educational impulses ran deep and were not confined to music. Ever
mindful of his impoverished childhood, he instinctively sought to correct what he
saw as incipient complacency in children from more privileged homes, though here
his methods were not so enlightened. His friend and biographer-to-be Max Kalbeck
recalled in later years:

*One Christmas while my wife and I were away from home, Brahms came to the house
with his pockets full. But when he saw the many luxurious presents with which, sorely
against our wills, the children had been surfeited by friends, he gave each of them a
slap, and went away grumbling.*

It says much for him, and for them, that they continued to love him in spite of his
strange, unpredictable behaviour. It was probably just as well, however, that he
never became a father.

# Brahms and the Piano

From early boyhood, as we've seen, the piano was never far from the centre of Brahms's musical life, and his works for it, whether solo or in company, effectively frame his entire career as a composer. The seldom heard E flat minor Scherzo, despite its publication as op. 4, is the earliest of Brahms's works to have survived, and its background remains obscure. Dating from 1851, when Brahms was eighteen, it was the first of the pieces that he chose to play to the Schumanns but remains the least evidently Brahmsian of all his works. Next came the three mighty and progressively more masterly Sonatas. Written successively, though not in the published order, they were completed in 1853, when he was twenty. High among their many remarkable features are the extraordinary individuality and integrity of Brahms's musical personality. That they were the products of a youth who still looked and sounded more like a child almost beggars belief. While all three have much to recommend them, the third, in F minor, is the only one to have secured a place near the centre of the concert repertory. Cast unusually in five movements, it demonstrates better than either of its predecessors Brahms's characteristic combination of passion, virtuosity and intellectual discipline. Its organic unity is remarkable, the first movement in particular deriving most of its material from the very opening idea, and the rapt, expansive coda of the second movement is among the most inspired passages ever conceived for the piano.

The four Ballades, op. 10 were written in the summer of 1854 and mark the beginning of Brahms's preoccupation with the self-contained lyrical piano piece, a genre to which many of his precursors in the romantic movement had contributed such a mountain of dross that its viability as a vehicle for serious music had been sorely damaged. In his own contributions, Brahms looks back, as so often, to Beethoven (notably the three sets of Bagatelles), Schubert (the Impromptus and *Moments musicaux*), Mendelssohn (*Songs Without Words*, etc.) and, to a lesser extent, Chopin. Schumann's many short piano pieces were less influential here than one might expect, since most of them appear as part of his multi-movement 'piano cycles' (*Papillons, Kinderscenen, Davidsbündlertänze, Carnaval, Kreisleriana, Faschingsschwank aus Wien*, etc.) and were never intended for separate performance.

When Schumann described Brahms's early, massive sonatas as 'veiled symphonies' he may have been even more perceptive than he knew. Interestingly, Brahms's long-awaited production of authentic symphonies in the middle 1870s signalled an end to his interest in the piano as a vehicle for large-scale designs. After the two-piano version of the so-called 'Haydn' Variations, he confined his solo piano writing to shorter (though by no means always 'miniature') pieces, published in successive groups, but generally without the organic cohesion of Schumann's piano suites. We get a foretaste of these in the delectable Waltzes, op. 39 of 1865. Nowhere, not even in his popular *Liebeslieder*, is Brahms less Germanic or more deliciously Viennese. Not that there aren't Germanic touches. Some of the pieces have a wildness, even a mock ferocity, unknown to the truly Viennese waltz, and only Brahms would conclude a cycle of seductive waltzes with an exercise in double counterpoint. It's a measure of their popularity that Brahms made three versions, two for piano solo, of which the first is far more difficult, and one for piano duet.

For a long time, the two Rhapsodies of 1879 were amongst the most popular and frequently performed of all Brahms's piano works. If his early sonatas were 'veiled symphonies', these large-scale though highly sectional pieces might equally be seen as veiled overtures. Seldom is Brahms's piano writing more orchestral in character. Despite the expressive abandon suggested by their title, both works are cast in a modified sonata form and speak a language of the utmost seriousness (indeed the second, in G minor, is almost grim in its implacable, march-like gait). At the same time, particularly in the B minor, there is a sweetness and poignancy which is uniquely Brahmsian.

With only a few exceptions, Brahms entitled most of his shorter piano pieces either 'Capriccio' or 'Intermezzo', the latter being a particularly confusing title since the term taken literally suggests one piece put between two others. To begin a group with an intermezzo is therefore a contradiction in terms, yet Brahms's op. 117 consists of nothing else. The eighteen pieces to which he gave the name have much in common and stand at the opposite extreme to the heroic cast of the early sonatas and the virtuosic grandeur and panache of the 'Handel' and 'Paganini' Variations. They are generally intimate in character, indeed they contain some of the tenderest and most poignantly affecting music ever penned, and they fall for the most part into a simple ternary (A–B–A) pattern, in which the opening music returns, usually with some subtle alteration, after a contrasting middle section. In their outer simplicity of utterance they often reflect Brahms's lifelong love affair with folk music – and his own strong identification with the 'folk' – but they often contain harmonic and rhythmic features of enormous sophistication and subtlety. With the sole exception of op. 76, the first of his piano 'suites' (written in 1878, the year of the great Violin Concerto), they are late pieces, composed mainly between 1891 and 1893, and give us Brahms at his richest and most masterly.

*Brahms's piano room at 4 Karlgasse, Vienna. Even here he had Beethoven looking over his shoulder. Aquarelle by Wilhelm Nowak, 1904.*

While the intermezzos are serious (though rarely solemn) in tone, the capriccios ('caprices') give us the more outward bound, unbuttoned Brahms, sometimes playful, even coquettish, sometimes brusque, sometimes, indeed, almost violent. Here, more on the whole than in the intermezzos, we encounter Brahms's fascination with rhythmic games – and that term isn't as flippant as it may sound. Music, after

all, is the only sphere in which we 'play' 'works'. In much great music, and much *serious* music to boot, there is often a very considerable degree of game-playing. In this instance it involves such devices as writing 'against' the metre, making us feel two-beat groups in a prevailing context of three, or groups of one kind actually superimposed on groups of another, so that we hear both at once, 'in conflict', as it were – in some ways the aural equivalent of optical illusions, except that in music it's the composer who controls our perceptions. There's a good example of this (and very much in the spirit of a game, too) in the third of the Four Piano Pieces, op. 119 [on CD3], and still better examples in the C sharp minor Capriccio, op. 76 no. 5, and the opening D minor Capriccio of op. 116. These so-called 'cross rhythms' are in many ways the bread and butter of Brahms's overall style. Of the short pieces under discussion, hardly any are rhythmically straightforward. No other piano composer of the nineteenth century used rhythm in such complex and teasing combinations as Brahms. It can be effortlessly light-hearted, as in that C major Intermezzo of op. 119, or used to highly dramatic and turbulent effect, as in op. 76 no. 5 just mentioned.

In striking contrast with the piano works of Chopin and Liszt, Brahms's keyboard writing is sometimes almost severe in its avoidance of decorative embellishment, possibly on the undeniable grounds that there is already so much for the ear to perceive in the way of rhythmic illusions, harmonic clashes resulting from the close overlapping of parts (just listen to the opening Intermezzo of op. 119 on CD3), colouristic devices nourished by very wide distances between the hands, pedalling of positively Debussyan subtlety (not for nothing did the great pianist Artur Schnabel call Brahms 'the first Impressionist'), and the frequent intertwining of melodic strands whose contrapuntal ingenuity is worthy of Bach.

# CHAPTER 4

# The External Brahms

*Like the trousers of a true countryman, his own were always hitched up to ankle height. When a tailor, secretly egged on by Brahmins\*, was bold enough to make them the proper length in defiance of orders, Brahms attacked the Gordian pants with his desk shears and simply cut them to ankle length.*

Robert Haven Schauffler in *The Unknown Brahms*

From the time of Schumann's panegyric† onwards, Brahms was a celebrity whether he liked it or not. And though he cultivated an increasingly prickly exterior (harmonizing nicely with his favourite Viennese haunt, the Red Hedgehog), there were times when he liked it quite a lot. While he valued solitude, indeed depended on it, as most creative artists must, he placed no premium on loneliness. Reserved, often suspicious, and fiercely private, he was also naturally convivial, at times even gregarious. And he was no ivory-tower composer, either, but a deeply communicative one, with a deeply human pleasure in being appreciated. In any case, no one embracing the career of performer, as the young Brahms unequivocally did, can be wholly indifferent to fame. And whatever its internal effects, it fundamentally determines the way in which the famous are perceived by others.

In his middle twenties, those freshly encountering Brahms were struck above all

*The jesting nickname popularly given to Brahms's most devout worshippers.
†See p. 79.

else by the extraordinary disparity between the god-like 'young eagle' described by
Schumann and the small, unassuming youth they now beheld. In 1857, the cellist
Julius Schmidt described the outer Brahms, then twenty-four, as 'so delicate and
refined as to be almost girlish – an impression strengthened by his voice, which
was still of the high quality so often mentioned'. It was at about this time that
Brahms, increasingly embarrassed by this unwelcome peculiarity, began to practise
a series of vocal gymnastics which succeeded somewhat in forcing down the pitch
but left him hoarse for life.*

In 1865, the Swiss poet Joseph Widmann, who was to become a lifelong friend,
saw Brahms for the first time and was transfixed:

*The boyish (or even girlish) Brahms at 20, the time of his first meeting with Schumann. It's hard to believe that this childlike, high-voiced youth had already composed his three 'veiled symphonies' (see pp. 57–8). Sepia sketch by J. J. B. Laurens.*

*Brahms was less than candid on this subject as the years went by. In 1877 he told the
composer Richard Heuberger 'that he had had a very good soprano voice as a boy, but had
spoilt it by singing too much'.

*Brahms, then in his thirty-third year, immediately gave me the impression of a gigantic personality, not alone because of his powerful piano playing, with which no virtuoso technique, no matter how brilliant, could be compared, but also through his personal appearance. It is true that the short, somewhat stocky figure, the almost straw-blond hair, and the protruding lower lip which imparted an almost sarcastic expression to his beardless face, were conspicuous features which might rather displease. His whole presence, however, seemed suffused with power. The broad leonine chest, the Herculean shoulders, the mighty head which he occasionally threw back with an energetic toss while playing, the pensive, well-formed forehead radiant as if by some inner illumination, and the Germanic eyes which sparkled a miraculous fire between their blond lashes – all betrayed an artistic personality which seemed charged to its very fingertips with the power of genius.*

Can this be the same person depicted by Schmidt only eight years earlier? The accuracy of Widmann's description is borne out by Georg Henschel's impressions nine years later, by which time all traces of Schmidt's 'delicate', 'refined', 'girlish' youth had long since vanished.

*He was broad-chested, of short stature, with a tendency to stoutness. His face was clean-shaven, revealing a rather thick, genial underlip; the healthy and ruddy colour of his skin indicated a love of nature and a habit of being in the open air in all kinds of weather; his thick straight hair of brownish colour came nearly down to his shoulders. His clothes and boots were not exactly of the latest pattern, nor did they fit particularly well. What, however, struck me most was the kindliness of his eyes. They were of a light blue; wonderfully keen and bright, with now and then a roguish twinkle in them, and yet at times an almost childlike tenderness. Soon I was to find out that the roguish twinkle in his eyes corresponded to a quality in his nature which would perhaps be best described as good-natured sarcasm.*

It was in 1871, when he was thirty-eight, that Florence May first met him, and her description is characteristically feminine in the subtlety of its perceptions:

*His most striking physical characteristic was the grand head with its magnificent intellectual forehead, but the blue eyes were also remarkable from their expression of intense mental concentration. He was near-sighted, and made frequent use of a double eyeglass that he wore hanging on a thin black cord round his neck. When walking out, it was his custom to go bareheaded, and to carry his soft felt hat in his hand, swinging the arm energetically to and fro. The disengaged hand he often held behind him. In Brahms's demeanour there was a mixture of sociability and reserve which gave the impression of a kindly-natured man, but one whom it would be difficult really to know. Though always pleasant and friendly, yet there was something about him – perhaps it may have been his extraordinary dislike of speaking about himself – which suggested that his life had not been free from disappointment, and that he had reckoned with the latter and taken his course. His manner was absolutely simple and unaffected.*

In view of the notorious rudeness associated with Brahms by posterity, it's interesting to find both these witnesses alighting on his evident kindliness as a key factor in their impressions.

Nine years later, Ferruccio Busoni, still some way short of his twentieth birthday, formed a more penetrating impression. Brahms, he wrote,

*looks like a sturdy German professor. Wears a full, grey beard, rather long hair, spectacles, moves gravely and leisurely – a habit assumed with the increase of years and circumference – and walks with his hands behind his back. Even if cold and brusque in temperament, he knows how to be kind (in his own way) and takes his place merrily at a well-victualled table. Under an apparent modesty, which his temperament doesn't allow to be ruffled, he hides a good conceit of himself (mainly justified). This mask of modesty materializes in constantly repelling each word received in his praise – by a shaking of the head, or by mumbling an unfinished word, or by suddenly changing the subject. Not because he believes himself unworthy of such praise but because he often has to rebuff tributes from incompetent quarters. Also he is reluctant to give indications about performance of his works, even if asked; not because of lack of belief in his own compositions but because he evidently regards such comments as a waste of time. Such, at least, are the impressions I've received. From time to time an ill-restrained irony peeps through: thus, for example, he deals with an insincere compliment.*

Given his fondness for long walks, in which few could keep pace with him, one can only attribute his increasing girth to his almost equal fondness for food and drink. Kalbeck's daughter was a frequent witness to his jovial appetite.

*I see, in my mind's eye, a well-stocked table full of variegated glasses and bottles. Father walks about and keeps on filling the guests' glasses. My brother and I see all this through the open door. There, at the head of the table sits the uncle with the long white flowing beard. The laughter with which he signs receipts for jokes roars its way out to us. Yes, Uncle Brahms could certainly drink and eat! Mother would have a big herring salad ready made for him and he would spoon the whole dish empty because he loved it so ... He was especially fond of that coarse proletarian dish, Rindspilaw [beef pilaf]. One summer at the Hotel Post in Ischl, when certain too-elegant visitors had deprived him of this for days, he ordered three portions of it, and dispatched them one after the other.*

*(right) Brahms at 27, much matured since Laurens's drawing of seven years earlier. In later years, he was seldom so well dressed. Oil painting ( from a photograph) by Josef Novak.*

According to his housekeeper, the typical Brahmsian supper consisted of a *kalter Aufschnitt* (a special selection of cold meats), and a tin of French sardines. The latter he always bought for himself, carrying it home in his coat-tail pocket. When the sardines were opened he would drink the oil directly out of the can 'at a draught', as one eye-witness put it. At no time, however, could he be suspected of a sedentary disposition. As Henschel observed in 1876:

*His solid frame, the healthy dark-brown colour of his face, the full hair, just a little sprinkled with grey, all make him appear the very image of strength and vigour. He walks about just as he pleases, with his waistcoat unbuttoned and his hat in his hand, always with clean linen, but without collar or necktie. These he dons at table d'hôte only. His whole appearance vividly recalls some of the portraits of Beethoven ... He eats with great gusto and in the evening regularly drinks his three glasses of beer,\* never omitting to finish off with his beloved* Kaffee.

As Henschel tells us, and as countless photographs, portraits and sketches confirm, visual comparisons with Beethoven were soon to be a thing of the past (apart from Brahms's habit of walking with his hands behind his back):

*In 1878 Brahms had considerably changed his outward appearance by the growth of the long and flowing beard in the frame of which his face has become familiar to the last and present generations. At the end of a concert in Vienna, Brüll and I were receiving in the artists' room the congratulations of friends, when suddenly I saw a man unknown to me, rather stout, of middle height, with long hair and a full beard, coming towards me. In a very deep, hoarse voice, he introduced himself – 'Musik-Direktor Müller' – making a very stiff and formal bow, which I was on the point of returning with equal gravity, when, an instant later, we all found ourselves laughing heartily at the perfect success of Brahms's disguise.*

To many of his friends, including Clara Schumann, the beard, whatever his motives for growing it, was a regrettable development. Characteristically, Brahms himself offered no explanation other than his preposterous claim to Widmann that 'one is taken for an actor or a priest if one is clean shaven'. By that token, he had suffered these misapprehensions in silence for more than two decades. As in so many other cases, the beard intensified the aura of paradox that surrounded Brahms throughout his adult life. At once, it was both a means of concealment and a way of calling attention to himself. This was no mere beard, but a super-beard, longer,

(right) In 1889, on a visit to Johann Strauss II at Bad Ischl. Note the omnipresent coffee and cigar. Photograph by R. Krziwanek.

*Thus do eye-witnesses differ: according to Max Friedländer, 'Brahms was usually a temperate person. He never drank in his own home. At the Red Hedgehog where he ate, his ration was one glass of wine and charged water. But in society he would drink with enthusiasm.'

more unruly and more luxuriant, in its faintly tramp-like way, than those sported by most others in his circle. By concealing most of his face, however (or having that effect), it accentuated what was in any case his most expressive feature. When the young Ethel Smyth arrived in Leipzig in 1878 to continue her musical studies, she soon met Brahms at the home of their mutual friends, the Herzogenbergs. As she wrote many years later:

*I only remember a strong, alarming face, very penetrating blue eyes, and my own desire to sink through the floor when he said, as I then thought by way of a compliment, but as I now know in a spirit of scathing irony, 'So this is the young lady who writes sonatas and doesn't know counterpoint!'*

As he grew older, his fame progressing steadily, Brahms seems to have taken less and less care of his appearance. Not for him the dandified elegance of a Chopin. He was not, however, merely negligent. Mindful of his childhood and youth, and proudly conscious of his ancestral roots, he often made a special point of emphasizing his solidarity with the poor and the so-called working class. Indeed in his adopted Vienna he must have cut a very curious figure indeed. 'I live in town as if I were in the country,' he once said (though he was a city-dweller born and bred and had never himself lived in the country, except on holiday). But as Mrs Frederick Partington remarked, he certainly looked the part. 'When I met him in 1888, he had a pleasant, ruddy, outdoor complexion. He was so burly and florid that he looked more like a farmer than like a man who spent his days in writing music.' His hands, too, were hard and rough to the touch, a fact attested to by many and unconvincingly ascribed by one observer to his 'economy in gloves'.

That 'ruddy, outdoor complexion' was honestly acquired, and not only on his long cross-country wanderings. 'For his noon meals,' Widmann reports,

*Brahms went to some outdoor restaurant whenever the weather permitted. He always disliked eating at the table d'hôte and avoided it whenever possible for the simple reason that he didn't like to get dressed up. He felt most comfortable in a striped woollen shirt without collar and without a necktie. Even his soft felt hat [a quaint, almost clownish second cousin to a bowler] was more often carried than worn. Whenever he came to stay, he would carry a leather travelling case which resembled a mineralogist's specimen bag filled with rocks, but which primarily contained the books I had lent him the previous week, which he brought back to be exchanged for others. In bad weather an old, brownish grey plaid held together in front by an enormous pin, hung over his shoulders and completed his queer, unstylish appearance, causing people to stare at him in astonishment.*

Writing of Brahms in 1886, Florence May employed that tact and understatement for which Britain in those days was still renowned. 'Brahms's ordinary costume was chosen quite without regard to appearances. Mere lapse of time must occasionally have compelled him to wear a new coat, but it is safe to conclude that his feelings suffered discomposure on the rare occurrence of such a crisis. Neckties and white collars were reserved as special marks of deference to conventionality.'

Deference to conventionality was one thing, kowtowing to the merely rich was quite another. When invited by its incumbent to visit a ducal palace at Gmunden in Austria, Brahms declined, protesting that he had no dress coat. The duke at once dispatched a message emphasizing that it was Brahms who was wanted, not his clothes, and that he should come as he was. Accordingly, the composer arrived in his usual faded, flannel shirt (collarless, thus also tie-less), and an elderly pair of trousers, hitched up, in best peasant tradition, to ankle height. He was at least, however, wearing socks on this occasion, which was by no means always so. The clothes can still be seen at the Gmunden Museum and bear mute witness to his Spartan economy. The right elbow of his faded alpaca coat, worn thin by long hours of composition at his desk, is reinforced with patches and crudely executed mends (presumably by Brahms himself), while the baggy black trousers bear a large brown patch on the seat and a corresponding black one at the front.

In 1881, Clara Schumann naively proposed to give Brahms a new suitcase. With cordial greetings, he declined: 'My best thanks for your friendly idea of buying me a travelling bag. However, what I have in that line really ought to do me. Truly I am a person so far from being spoiled and sophisticated that such a gift would be sheer waste.'

According to Robert Schauffler, his normal method of packing for a journey was 'to pile all his clothes upon a table and then tilt it so that everything spilled helter-skelter into an open trunk'.

# Brahms and the Orchestra

There is no aspect of Brahms's craftsmanship more consistently abused than his writing for orchestra. Before considering why, there are two important points to consider. Firstly, with the sole exception of the two serenades, which as we shall see are something of a special case, every note of Brahms's orchestral music has held its place at the centre of the repertoire from his time to our own without exception, and in the face of many dramatic swings of criticism and fashion. The same cannot be said of Mendelssohn, Berlioz, Liszt, Schumann, Bruckner, Mahler or Strauss. Secondly, those critics who have most persistently carped at Brahms's orchestration have never been remotely his equal in genius, skill, experience or musical insight. Is it likely that he himself was unable to detect in his own scores, on which he lavished so much unsparing self-criticism, the glaring 'faults' at which generations of pedantic nonentities have queued up to wag their reprimanding fingers? Or could it be that the most notoriously self-critical great composer in history wrote down exactly what he intended, in the full knowledge of its likely or certain effects? Could it be, further, that the blame might more justly be laid at the door of his interpreters?

A quick trawl of the evidence: Brahms wrote thirteen orchestral works: the four concertos, the serenades, two concert overtures, the so-called 'Haydn' Variations and, most importantly of all, the four symphonies. After the huge and hugely ambitious D minor Piano Concerto of 1859, there was a lull, in which he produced the

two unassuming orchestral serenades which are in some respects more like chamber music than anything symphonic. Indeed the first of them, in D, was originally conceived as a Nonet. The second, in A, is unusually scored for an orchestra without violins. Once having expanded the first into orchestral form, Brahms obviously had qualms about it. As he wrote to Joachim, 'I think I need to change my first serenade, now and finally, into a symphony. I can see that it isn't right to have it in this mongrel state. But I had such a beautiful, big conception of my first symphony, and now! ...' As it happened, he retained his beautiful big conception and the serenade remained a mongrel. And though its star has somewhat faded now, it achieved considerable popularity in its day. Between the Serenades and Brahms's next orchestral outing (excepting the accompanied choral works) lie thirteen years. In the fourteen between 1873 and 1887 came ten important works, and the rest is silence. In the last decade of his life Brahms turned his back on the orchestra, though there were rumours that he was contemplating a fifth symphony.

The great set of Variations on a Theme of Haydn, which broke the fast, as it were, was a hit from the start, and has remained so ever since. In more than a purely orchestral sense it can be seen as a kind of dry run for the symphonies. The layout is distinctly symphonic, the first three variations, with their bustling energy and vigour, standing in for a first movement, the fourth (an Andante in the minor mode) suggesting a slow second movement, the next three standing (or dancing) as a kind

*Brahms, Johann Strauss and Hans Richter at play, Brahms characteristically impassioned. Silhouette by Otto Böhler.*

of undercover Scherzo, and the Finale anticipating the passacaglia which crowns the Fourth Symphony by turning the theme into a so-called 'ground bass' and building up a splendid head of steam before the triumphant return of the original material.

Brahms's first true symphony, a good one and a half decades in the making, must have been the most keenly awaited in musical history. Its protracted gestation was due to three main causes: one was the continuing weight of Schumann's prophecy, another was the onus put on him by his own misguided 'manifesto' against the Neo-German school of Liszt and Wagner (see p. 140), but far and away the most powerful was the inspiring but inhibiting example of Beethoven, whose natural heir he was widely felt to be. And what did the critics tell him now that he had finally taken the plunge? – 'The most striking motif of this whole tedious work, the leading theme of the last movement, is so much like the Finale of Beethoven's Ninth Symphony that it should be put in quotation marks.' The same observation was widely made by journalistic scribes on both sides of the Atlantic, though most listeners today may wonder why (the theme, like the movement itself, being at least as remarkable for its differences from Beethoven). And even well-meant observations had their sting in the tail: to have his First Symphony described as 'Beethoven's Tenth' (which it was, by Hans von Bülow) was at best a mixed blessing. Nevertheless, he'd now crossed the Rubicon, and the Second Symphony came as easily as the First had come hard. Between the Second and Third came the instantly popular Academic Festival Overture, its darker sibling the Tragic Overture, the Violin Concerto and the Second Piano Concerto (see p. 43), all of them replete with orchestration perfectly matched to their musical function and character.

*Two hedgehogs – one large, the other small. Brahms on the way to his favourite Viennese watering hole, the Red Hedgehog. Caricature by Otto Böhler.*

The commonest charge against Brahms's orchestration is that it is 'thick', 'glutin-ous', 'stodgy'. According to one prominent conductor, no longer with us, 'the sun never shines in it'. How anyone can maintain such an opinion after hearing the Second Symphony or the wonderful, buoyant Finale of the B flat Concerto is difficult to understand. But let the matter be put into the context of the time, and of Brahms's own artistic personality.

There's no denying that Brahms quite consciously turned his back on the brilliant instrumentation of such nineteenth-century orchestral virtuosos as Berlioz, Wagner and Rimsky-Korsakov, but we may presume that it was for the same reasons that he rejected the whole concept of 'programme' music and other forms of artistic miscegenation: he deplored anything which distracted from the substance of music itself and was puritanically opposed to the use of any artistic resource for its own sake (including such fundamental disciplines as counterpoint and rhythm, of which he himself was a sovereign master). So much the worse if it was of a 'sensuous', superficial or sensational character. Not that his own instrumentation is particularly austere. There are many instances of the greatest tonal beauty in his music, but it is invariably used as a means to an end. The essence of Brahms's music is melodic, harmonic, rhythmic, contrapuntal, structural (no composer of the period so rigor-ously applied the discipline of form to emotional expression). Consequently he will often use a particular scoring not principally for colouristic purposes but as a means of structural emphasis.

As may be seen from his personal life, he had a marked distaste for extravagance, in an age fairly besotted by it. Not for him the ever-expanding orchestral forces of Wagner, Bruckner, Mahler and Strauss. Brahms's orchestra is not significantly different from Beethoven's because it doesn't need to be. The evolution of his instru-mentation through the years does not reflect a crawl from ineptitude to competence, but his own evolving aims. The changes in orchestration result precisely from the changes in the music. Interestingly, the darker, deeper, denser, lower-toned orches-tration of the D minor Concerto and the Serenades coincides with that period when he was most embarrassed by the high pitch of his speaking voice. The lighter, more translucent scoring of the B flat Concerto and much of the Second Symphony date from a time when, at considerable cost to his vocal cords, he had forced his voice downwards to the hoarse growl associated with his maturity.

# CHAPTER 5

# Brahms as Composer

*Without inner cohesion, without the most intimate connection of each and every part, music is nothing but a sandheap, incapable of any lasting impression. Inner cohesion alone can make of it the solid marble, on which the hand of the artist may immortalize itself.*

G. E. Lessing, copied by Brahms into his quotation book in 1855

Just when Brahms began to compose we shall never know. His reluctance to discuss either his early life or his creative faculties bordered on the pathological. At the height of his celebrity he was asked to fill in a biographical questionnaire. 'Impossible,' he replied. 'I would have to paint nothing but zeros and dashes in these columns. I have had no experiences that I could communicate. I have attended no high schools or musical institutions for musical culture. I have embarked on no travels for purposes of study. I have received no instruction from eminent masters. I am the incumbent of no public offices. Well, then, what am I to write here?' Brahms was never a braggart, and it would hardly have been in character for him to fabricate evidence of his own precocity, yet there is something faintly improbable about his claim to have invented his own system of notation 'before I realized that one had already long been in existence'. Is it likely that the son of a multi-instrumentalist professional musician, living in cramped quarters, would never have seen any printed music lying about the house? Whatever the truth of the matter, it seems safe to assume that Brahms was composing in his head long before he set pen to paper. We've seen that Cossel, whose brief was to groom him as a pianist, worried that Brahms's determination to compose might unduly distract him from his 'proper', instrumental studies, as we have also seen that Marxsen positively encouraged it. We have it on the authority of the pianist–song-writer Louise Japha that the eleven-year-old Brahms played her a full-blown piano sonata of his own, but like so many of his later compositions this seems to have been systematically incinerated. Other victims of Brahms's notorious incendiary zeal at this time were the 'Fantasia upon a Favourite Waltz' which he played at his Hamburg recital of 1849, two more piano sonatas, a duo for cello and piano, a fantasy in D minor for piano trio, a violin sonata and a string quartet. Among the few survivors are the Scherzo in E flat minor, composed when he was eighteen and later published as his op. 4, two studies after Chopin and Weber, and, most curiously, the *Souvenir de la Russie* (fantasy transcriptions of Russian and Bohemian airs for piano duet) which he published in 1850 as 'op. 151' by 'G. W. Marks'. This was one of a number of arrangements and pot-pourris issued under that name by the Hamburg light-music publisher Cranz. The same pseudonym hid the identities of a number of local composers, of whom Brahms's teacher Marxsen was almost certainly one. It was all unabashed hack work, hence the all-purpose moniker, but it brought in a little extra money and provided Brahms with some useful compositional practice. Hack work or otherwise, it demonstrates that Brahms, for all his preponderantly serious and old-fashioned inclinations (evident even in his earliest teenage years), was thoroughly conversant with the popular music of his day, and did not despise it. It was partly through this work, supplemented by the practices of his teachers, that Brahms developed his early and pervasive enthusiasm for folk music, little guessing, perhaps, what a major force it was to become in the music of his maturity.

But it wasn't all music. Like most nineteenth-century composers, he was substantially influenced by literature, and the greatest hero of his teenage years was E. T. A. Hoffmann.* Like Schumann before him (though Brahms didn't yet know this), he was particularly entranced by Hoffmann's novel *Kater Murr*, especially by its central character, the eccentric, half-mad Kapellmeister Kreisler, who shunned the coarse, uncaring society about him and idealistically took refuge in his art. The characters of Kreisler and the latter-day Philistines were immortalized for musicians in Schumann's piano cycles *Kreisleriana* and *Carnaval*. The young Brahms now went one better and began to sign himself 'Johannes Kreisler Junior' – a practice which stayed with him, on and off, until as late as 1860.

*The stories of this fascinating writer–musician–lawyer were a touchstone of the early romantics and provided the basis for Tchaikovsky's *Nutcracker*, Delibes's *Coppelia* and, most obviously, Offenbach's *Tales of Hoffmann*.

Curiously enough it was at the hand of Schumann himself that Brahms experienced his first serious musical disappointment. When the great man visited Hamburg in 1850 the seventeen-year-old composer, to whom most of Schumann's works were still unknown, sent a parcel of his own compositions to Schumann's hotel. It was returned unopened. Little can anyone have guessed at the time how spectacularly Schumann was to make amends for this unintended slight.

*Clara Schumann in her early 20s. She was already one of the world's greatest pianists. Coloured lithograph by Straub.*

\*

We left the touring Brahms in Bonn (p. 30). It was September 1853. He was twenty years old and making new and influential friends at every port of call, among them the violinist and conductor Wasielewski, who gave him a letter of introduction to the music-loving Deichmann family in Mehlem. Through them he made the acquaintance of a number of eminent musicians, among them Franz Wüllner, Ferdinand Hiller and Carl Reinecke, and it was in their home that he first had the chance to study Schumann's works, most of which, including *Kreisleriana*, were new to him. On almost every page he found a kindred spirit so close as to be uncanny. With images of his unopened parcel now banished from his mind, he bade a series of farewells to his friends in Mehlem and set out for Düsseldorf, drawn to Schumann's door as by a magnet. On the last day of September he stood before the house – no Altenburg, but a comfortable, middle-class German home – and rang the bell. The door was opened by a little girl. Her parents were not at home, but he would find them in if he called again next day at eleven o'clock. Next day, he returned as bidden.

With the sound of children in the background, he was instantly made welcome. He and Schumann talked together naturally, unaffected by the twenty-three-year difference in their ages, and Brahms was invited to play. He began with his recently completed C major Sonata but had not got far into it when Schumann interrupted him. 'Please, please; one moment. My wife.' He left the room. 'Clara!' he called out. 'Come! You must hear this!' At thirty-four, Clara Schumann, *née* Wieck, was widely held to be among the greatest pianists of the century. Chopin had said of her, 'She is the only woman in Germany who can play my music.' Yet Brahms felt none of the inhibition and discomfort that had assailed him at Liszt's. Here, in the double presence of genius, he felt only exaltation. 'Now,' said Schumann to his wife. 'Now you will hear music such as you have never heard before.' That day at lunch, the Schumann children found their parents in a state of scarcely containable euphoria. That evening, Schumann wrote tersely in his diary: 'Visit from Brahms – a genius.' Clara, in hers, was more expansive:

*Here is one who seems to have come straight from God. He played us sonatas, scherzos, etc. of his own, all of them showing exuberant imagination, depth of feeling, and mastery of form. Robert says that there was nothing that he could tell him to take*

*A pensive Schumann in his early 40s, a few years before meeting Brahms. Coloured engraving after a drawing by Eduard Bendemann.*

*away or to add. It is really very moving to see him sitting at the piano, with his interesting young face, which becomes transfigured when he plays, his beautiful hands, which overcome the greatest difficulties with perfect ease (his things are very difficult), and in addition these remarkable compositions. He has studied with Marxsen in Hamburg but what he played to us is so masterly that one cannot but think that the good God sent him into the world ready-made. He has a great future ahead of him, for he will first find the true field for his genius when he begins to write for the orchestra. Robert says there is nothing to wish except that heaven preserve his health.*

Brahms, for his part, having now met his recently discovered mentor, wrote ecstatically to a friend:

*What am I to tell you of Schumann? Shall I break into panegyrics on his genius and his character? Or shall I lament that mankind once again commits the great sin of in many ways misjudging and doing small honour to a good man and divine artist? And I myself, how long did I not commit this sin? Not until after my departure from Hamburg, during my sojourn at Mehlem, did I come to know and pay homage to the works of Schumann. I feel I ought to crave his pardon . . . Their praise has made me feel so glad and strong that I hardly know how to wait for the time when at last I shall be able to work and to create undisturbed.*

The wait, as it happened, was considerably extended by Schumann himself. If he had been terse in his diary, he could hardly have been less so in a long article which he wrote for the *Neue Zeitschrift für Musik* which he had founded in 1834 and which under his impassioned editorship of ten years and more had become one of the most influential musical journals in Germany. He had begun his journalistic career by recognizing the true stature of Chopin in an article whose opening words, 'Hats off, gentleman! A genius!' may well be the most famous utterance in the history of musical criticism. He now closed it (though he didn't know it at the time) by doing the same for Brahms. In an article entitled 'Neue Bahnen' (New Pathways), he hailed this hitherto unknown young man of twenty as a musical Messiah.

*It seemed to me . . . that there would and indeed must suddenly appear one man who would be singled out to articulate and give the ideal expression to the tendencies of our time, one man who would show us his mastery, not through a gradual process, but, like Minerva, springing fully armed from the head of Zeus. And he has come, a young man over whose cradle Graces and Heroes stood guard. His name is Johannes Brahms and he comes from Hamburg, where he has been working in quiet obscurity. He carries all the marks of one who has received a call. Seated at the piano, he began to disclose the most wonderful regions . . . There were sonatas, or rather veiled symphonies; songs whose poetry would be clear even if one were ignorant of the words, though a profound singing melody runs through them all; individual piano pieces of an almost demonic nature and charming form; then sonatas for violin and piano, quartets for strings – and all so different from one another that each seemed to flow from a fresh spring . . .*

*When he waves his magic wand where the power of great orchestral and choral masses will aid him, then we shall be shown still more wonderful glimpses into the secrets of the spirit-world. May the highest Genius strengthen him for this . . . His contemporaries salute him on his first journey through the world where wounds may await him, but also palms and laurels; we welcome him as a powerful fighter.*

What had Brahms said to Joachim? 'I cannot consider returning to Hamburg with nothing to show . . . I must at least have two or three compositions in print, so that I can cheerfully look my parents in the face.' Suddenly, quite literally over-night, he was famous. His name was on the lips of every musician in Germany, publishers were queueing up to get their hands on his works, and he was now in the unenviable position of having to live up to impossible expectations. His already chronic perfectionism had seen to it that the works he had to show were few, and he was by no means ready to release them all for public scrutiny. Almost three weeks after reading Schumann's unexpected panegyric (the lapse of time suggesting a measure of confused ambivalence), Brahms wrote to him:

*Honoured Master, You have made me so immensely happy that I cannot attempt to thank you in words. God grant that my works may soon prove to you how much your affection and kindness have encouraged and stimulated me. The public praise you have deigned to bestow on me will have so greatly increased the musical world's expectations of my work that I do not know how I shall manage to do even approximate justice to it. Above all it forces me to exercise the greatest caution in the choice of pieces for publication.*

The first to bite the dust were two trios and a string quartet in B flat, of which Brahms, with characteristic thoroughness, expunged all trace. Spared were his three Piano Sonatas, the lone Scherzo in E flat minor and a group of songs, including the soon-to-be-famous 'Liebestreu'.

Wherever he now went, the reserved and self-effacing twenty-year-old found himself the object of curious scrutiny, and frequently, too, of a pronounced scepti-cism. As Arnold Schloenbach put it at the time, 'Schumann's article had awakened mistrust in numerous circles. At all events it had created a very difficult situation for the young man, for its justification required the fulfilment of great demands; and when the slender, fair youth appeared, so deficient in presence, so shy, so modest, his voice still in transitional falsetto, few could have suspected the genius that had already created so rich a world in this young nature.' Almost invariably, he was not what people expected. In the diary of Hedwig Salomon, a wealthy music lover and patroness, we read:

*Yesterday Herr von Sahr brought to me a young man who held in his hand a letter from Joachim. There he was before me, Schumann's young Messiah, fair and delicate; though only in his twentieth year, his face showed the triumph of his spirit. Purity, innocence, naturalness, power, and depth – this describes his character. Schumann's prophecy tempts one perhaps to find him rather absurd, and to be severe with him, but one forgets everything, and loves and admires him without restraint. And with all this independent strength, a thin boy's voice that has not changed and a child's countenance that any girl might kiss without blushing. And the purity and firmness of his whole being, which guarantee that the spoiled world will not be able to overcome this man; for, as he has been able to bear his elevation from obscurity to the perilous position of an idol without losing any of his modesty, or even his naivety, so God who created such a beautiful nature will continue to help him!*

And from Herr von Sahr himself: 'He is perfect! The days since he has been here are amongst the most delightful in my recollection. He answers exactly to my idea of an artist. And as a man!'

One effect of Schumann's article had been to diminish at a stroke the sheer pleasure and emotional release which Brahms had previously, though not consistently, found in the act of composition. From 1853 onwards, he carried the weight of destiny on his shoulders. Between the publications of 1853–4* and 1860, the musical world waited, apparently in vain, for the fulfilment of Schumann's ringing prophecy. Apart from the op. 10 Ballades (as noted on p. 31), he published nothing for six years. But he was far from idle. To those six years, and unremitting hard labour, we owe the great String Sextet in B flat, op. 18, the Variations on an Original Theme, op. 21, the Piano Quartet in G minor, op. 25, a number of choral works, and towering above them all, the great Piano Concerto no. 1 in D minor, op. 15.

In 1856, when he was twenty-three, he made perhaps the most intensive study of counterpoint ever undertaken by a great composer since the death of Bach in 1750. With extraordinary industry he lifted his already remarkable technique as a composer to a level of mastery achieved by very few in any era. At no time, however, did he rest content with craftsmanship alone. As he begged of Joachim, on sending him some canons, 'Quite apart from the skill in them, *are they good music*? Does the ingenuity make them more beautiful and valuable?'

*The three Piano Sonatas, the Scherzo, a number of songs, the Variations on a Theme of Schumann, op. 9, and the first version of the B major Trio, op. 8.

For his part, Schumann was puzzled and faintly anxious. In 1854 he wrote to Joachim, 'I am surprised that Brahms is working at counterpoint, which does not seem like him.' And again to Joachim, 'Is he flying high – or only amongst flowers? Is he putting drums and trumpets to work yet? He must remember the beginnings of the Beethoven symphonies; he must try to do something of the same kind. The point is to make a beginning.' But Schumann's unprecedented accolade had made this a great deal more easily said than done. In hailing Brahms's piano sonatas as 'veiled symphonies' he had scored one of his critical bull's-eyes, as he did in predicting that Brahms would soon find the keyboard inadequate to the immensity of his ideas. But it was typical of Brahms that he had to discover this for himself, and by a tortuous route. No more ironic example exists of age recalling youth through rose-tinted spectacles than Brahms's plaint near the end of his life, 'I have tormented myself to no purpose lately, and till now I never had to do so at all; *things always came easily to me*' [italics mine]. Contrast this with his melancholy plea to Clara in 1858, 'Do not wonder that I write you nothing about my work. I do not want to do it and cannot do it – I have so little disposition and desire to lament to others about my lack of genius and skill.' And two years later, still only in his middle twenties: 'If things are small, they are all the harder to make, as, unfortunately, everything is still difficult for me.' There is no reason to doubt his sincerity. Who else in history was to wrestle for fifteen years with his First Symphony before feeling ready to unveil it?

The slightly less extravagant vicissitudes of his First Piano Concerto are discussed elsewhere (see p. 150) but its slow evolution from a sonata for two pianos by way of a quickly abandoned symphony is as good an example as any of the uncertainties that typically lay beneath the surface of his most magnificently assertive and self-confident works. Partly because of its titanic stature, its epic scope and its prodigious craftsmanship, it's hard to remember that this is not only the work of a very young man but his first essay of any kind in an orchestral medium. There is no work in musical history more supremely self-assured, yet its road to fruition was fairly peppered with doubts and anxieties. It was a lifelong practice of Brahms's to beseech his friends for constructive advice, as when he wrote to Joachim during the composition of this work:

*I am sending you the rondo once more. And just like the last time, I beg for some really severe criticism. Some parts have been completely replaced – for the better, I hope – others merely changed. Especially the ending was improved; it was too sketchy and did not accomplish what it set out to do. One place I left untouched, although it bears a question mark on its forehead. Must it be removed, at all costs? In the first movement I have smoothed out a few of the weak passages. I did not quite succeed with the first one, and therefore left it alone, for the time being. I again enclose both movements; perhaps you can point out a few things I can improve ... In the Finale several episodes are still very thinly orchestrated. I am still so ignorant, and don't know how to help myself.*

Would anyone connect that sentence with the music in question? Or guess that only days before the first performance the composer wrote, again to Joachim, 'If you are willing and able, do please write me a few words to let me know whether the effort wasn't altogether futile, and whether it has any chance. I no longer have either judgement or control of the piece. Nothing decent will come of it anyway.'

Something very much more than decent did come of it, but the first performance of the work in Leipzig was in many ways a catastrophe for Brahms. Or would have been to one of lesser mettle. A similar critical débâcle in the case of Bizet's *Carmen* is widely thought to have precipitated that composer's tragic death at thirty-six. But to paraphrase Jerome Kern's popular song, Brahms picked himself up, dusted himself off and prepared to start all over. He made no pretence of being unhurt, but with a resilience characteristic of his genius he determined to profit from his own defeat. 'In spite of everything,' he wrote to Joachim, 'the Concerto will meet with approval when I have improved its form, and the next one will be quite different. I believe this is the best thing that can happen to one; it forces one to concentrate one's thoughts and increases one's courage. After all, I am only experimenting and feeling my way as yet.' And he knew with complete serenity that he was right about the concerto. So far from merely meeting with approval, it soon established itself, and has remained, ever since, one of the highest peaks of the mainstream concert repertory.*

The fact that Brahms seldom took the advice he so pleadingly solicited is no reason to doubt the sincerity of his gratitude, as when he told Joachim in the case of the D minor Concerto, 'Without you I could not have done it.' We get some measure of Joachim's involvement, and Brahms's perplexity, from an exchange of letters in the winter of 1858. In January, Brahms writes, 'Please send back to me my unhappy first movement, so incapable of being brought to birth.' And in February, Joachim replies:

*Brahms's many entreaties for help, advice and criticism were by no means a feature only of his youth. In 1877, when he could no longer plead ignorance or helplessness, we find him writing to Clara, 'I want to publish my songs [Lieder, op. 69–72] and should be so very much obliged if you could play them through beforehand and give me a word of advice about them. Write and tell me which of them pleases you, and whether you dislike any of them. Particularly in regard to the last, I might accept your criticism and thank you! ... If possible write me a short comment on each. You need only give the opus or the number; for instance, op. X, 5, bad; 6, outrageous; 7, ridiculous, and so on.'

*Here at last is your piece returned – I have looked it through again completely, and I must hope that the places with the altered orchestration please you. If that is not so, get hold of a good stick of india-rubber – which cannot be lacking in your Hamburg, proud ruler of the sea and islands. But, man, I do beg you for God's sake send it to the copyists; when shall I at last hear it?*

That Joachim so willingly, so thoughtfully and so repeatedly answered Brahms's almost compulsive entreaties is a tribute both to the man and to his friendship with one whose gifts he had recognized from the beginning were quite beyond his own. Fairly early on in their acquaintance, Joachim had made some remarkable observations of the relationship between the man and the composer:

*Brahms is egoism incarnate, without himself being aware of it. He bubbles over in his cheery way with exuberant thoughtlessness – but sometimes with a lack of consideration (not a lack of reserve, for that would please me!) which offends because it betrays a certain want of culture. He has never once troubled to consider what others, according to their natures and the course of their development, will hold in esteem; the things that do not arouse his enthusiasm, or that do not fit in with his experience, or even with his mood, are callously thrust aside, or, if he is in the humour, attacked with a malicious sarcasm . . . He knows the weaknesses of the people about him, and he makes use of them, and then does not hesitate to show (to their faces, I grant you) that he is crowing over them. His immediate surroundings are quite apart from his musical life, and from his attachment to a higher and more fantastic world. And the way in which he wards off all the morbid emotions and imaginary troubles of others is really delightful. He is absolutely sound in that, just as his complete indifference to the means of existence is beautiful, indeed magnificent. His compositions too are an easy treatment of the most difficult forms – so pregnant, rejecting all earthly sorrows with such indifference. I have never come across a talent like his before. He is miles ahead of me.*

Brahms, for his part, held his friend in the highest esteem, and was not dissembling when he wrote, at twenty-one, 'I feel so imbecile . . . I cannot understand how you can take any interest in my things.' The fact is that Brahms's 'things' were for Joachim a source not only of interest but of continuous enlightenment. He never doubted how much he himself could learn from Brahms, and his expressions of enthusiasm were unstinting but never sycophantic. After perusing Brahms's F minor Piano Quintet, he wrote, 'It is quite wonderful what you make of the themes! Altogether your second parts [i.e. developments and recapitulations], with all their multiplicity of counterpoint and fantasy come out as a perfectly unified whole.' In that one phrase, 'multiplicity of counterpoint and fantasy', lies one of the most important keys to understanding Brahms's music, be it as listener, interpreter or both. Brahms's style, being essentially polyphonic, is fundamentally melodic – hence expressive. His melody, however, is not confined to the upper voice, as in the standard accompanied song, but shared between the parts in an often sensuous intertwining perfectly suited to the prevailing ethos of romanticism. No other composer, not even Wagner or Bach, combined such contrapuntal mastery with so wide-ranging or mercurial an imaginative grasp – hence the fantasy.

*

There was no composer of whom Brahms stood in greater awe than Beethoven, nor any by whom he was so fundamentally influenced. And from the beginning of his career he was unafraid of paying his debts in public. To select as his op. 1 a sonata whose opening bars are conspicuously derived from the beginning of Beethoven's so-called 'Hammerklavier' (the Everest among his own, trail-blazing sonatas) was seen by some as a manifestation of hubris.* References to Beethoven, both overt and covert, recur in many of his subsequent works, most famously in the First Symphony, and in later years his name was commonly linked with those of Beethoven and Bach, and not just for their alliteration. Brahms himself was under no illusion that he was the equal of either and was more offended than flattered by the comparisons. As he said to his friend Georg Henschel in 1876:

*I am not ashamed to admit that it gives me the greatest pleasure if a song or an Adagio, or anything of mine, has turned out especially well. But how must those gods, Bach, Mozart and Beethoven have felt, whose daily bread it was to write things like the* St Matthew Passion, Don Giovanni, Fidelio, *the* Ninth Symphony! *What I cannot understand is how people like myself can possibly be vain. As much as we*

---

*Like his beloved mentor Schumann, though less coyly, Brahms enjoyed seasoning his works with (generally covert) allusions to other composers. Thus we find in his favourite song, 'Vergebliches Ständchen', a coded nod of gratitude to Mozart (see *The Marriage of Figaro*, Act III, Scene 5, at the words 'Höre, Geliebte'), and in another song, 'Der Gang zum Liebchen' (accompaniment), a clear reference to Chopin's C sharp minor Waltz. In the Third Symphony and the Second Piano Concerto there are clear, if enigmatic, references to Wagner's 'Venusberg' music, while the opening of the A major Violin Sonata quotes the 'Prize Song' from *Die Meistersinger* (in which opera Brahms himself is quoted. Wagner, whose diatribes against Brahms were extraordinarily venomous, used a theme from Brahms's F minor Piano Sonata for Hans Sach's first monologue in *Die Meistersinger*.) In the Scherzo of that sonata, however, Brahms himself poaches from Mendelssohn (Finale, C minor Trio). There are further Wagnerian references in Brahms's C minor String Quartet.

*men, who walk upright, are above the creeping things of the earth, so these gods are
above us. If it were not so ludicrous it would be loathsome to me to hear colleagues
praise me to my face in such an exaggerated manner.*

If the example of Beethoven was inspiring to him, it was no less intimidating ('You
don't know what it is like,' he wrote to Hermann Levi, 'always to hear that giant
marching along behind me.') It was this, more than his fear of not justifying Schumann's prophecies for him, that continually stayed his hand when he attempted to
write his first symphony. His first, abortive attempt on the challenge was the inter-
mediate stage, mentioned above, of the D minor Concerto; the second, close on its
heels, was an equivalent stage of his D major Serenade, which originated as a chamber work with only one instrument per part. In December 1858, he wrote to Joachim,
asking for supplies of lined paper for scoring (a luxury apparently unobtainable in
Detmold, where he was currently employed), with a view to reworking the serenade
into a symphony (see p. 72) but abandoned the attempt, worried that the original
concept was not 'beautiful' and 'big' enough for a symphony. Clearly he felt that he
owed it both to himself and to an expectant public to achieve something remarkable
with this first opus in the genre. The real First Symphony, when it finally appeared
almost eighteen years later [!], was indeed both beautiful and big. But there are dan-
gers, potentially fatal, in excessive perfectionism, as Brahms himself well knew. Of
his ravishing B flat String Sextet, an early work whose gestation was characteristically protracted, he wrote, 'If I had waited even longer, it could perhaps have been
better, but waiting has its own evils.' In composition, no less than any other branch
of creative endeavour, part of the art is knowing when to stop. With every passing
year, Brahms's struggle for the symphony grew more obsessive, despite the odd,
feigned attempt at escape. In 1875, he wrote to his friend Franz Wüllner, 'I stay sitting
here, and write from time to time highly useless pieces in order not to have to look
into the stern face of a symphony.' But by that time the long-awaited First was
actually nearing completion (and its opening could hardly have been sterner).

   That composition could be the most intense and strugglesome act for Brahms,
as for his idol Beethoven, is beyond question. Unlike Beethoven, however, as we've
seen, he left little of his method for posterity. As Eduard Hanslick remarked, 'It is
regrettable that Brahms was only very rarely and reluctantly induced to respond by
letter to musical questions. His profound musicological and technical knowledge,
combined with such clear, sharp judgement, could have provided a treasure trove
of information, whether he was speaking about his own projects and compositions
or those of others. Brahms was capable, in private conversation, of commenting on
musical matters with such fluidity and liveliness . . . yet with pen in hand he became
monosyllabic.' As for speaking about his own compositions or plans, his own

*Georg Henschel (later Sir George Henschel, as naturalized Briton) in his middle 20s. A distinguished singer, conductor and pianist, he became friendly with Brahms in 1874 and shared a holiday with him at Rügen in 1876.*

reticence held him back all his life. Just as sensitive was the response of his modesty to praise from others. His unwillingness to pass on flattering letters that had been sent to him was very difficult to overcome. But he did occasionally unburden himself, as to his fellow composer Henschel in 1876:

*One thing is certain. There is no creating without hard work. That which you would call invention, that is to say, a thought, an idea, is simply an inspiration from above, for which I am not responsible, which is no merit of mine. Yes, it is a present, a gift, which I ought even to despise until I have made it my own by right of hard work. And there is no hurry about that either. When I have found the first phrase of a song, say, I might shut the book there and then, go for a walk, do some other work, and perhaps not think of it again for months ... If, afterwards, I approach the subject again, it is sure to have taken shape; I can now really begin to work at it. But there are composers who sit at the piano with a poem before them, putting music to it from A to Z until it is done.*

This creative use of outwardly fallow periods, this willing surrender to apparent passivity, is one of the hallmarks of Brahms's artistic personality, calling to mind the old Russian proverb, 'We learn to swim in the winter and to ski in the summer.' And the summation of his advice to Henschel? 'Let it rest, let it rest, and keep going back to it and working at it over and over again until it is completed as a finished work of art, until there is not a note too much or too little, not a bar you could improve upon. Whether it is *beautiful* also, is an entirely different matter, but perfect it *must* be.'

Two fascinating vignettes of Brahms himself in the throes of creation come from his friend Max Kalbeck:

*Paying a morning visit to the house in the Salzburgerstrasse I went up the outside steps intending to come in by the wide-open back door when I saw that the door of the music room was also open. At that moment bewitching sounds came from the*

*Brahms's house at Bad Ischl, where he spent several summers and composed the Academic Festival and Tragic Overtures, many of the late piano pieces, opp. 116–19, the 2 Clarinet Sonatas, op. 120 and the 11 Chorale Preludes for organ – his last composition. Watercolour by Karl Blumauer, 1882.*

*piano which held me entranced on the doorstep. It sounded like free extemporization, but from the frequent repetitions of certain passages I realized that Brahms was going through and improving and refining a new composition already complete in his head. He repeated the piece several times in individual sections and eventually played it straight through ... The solo changed into an extraordinary duet. The richer the shaping of the work became, and the more passionately its delivery arose, so the more strongly could be heard a strange growling, whining and moaning that at the peak of the musical ecstasy became sheer howling. Could Brahms, quite contrary to his inclination, have got himself a dog? ... After about half an hour the playing and the howling stopped together, the piano stool was drawn back and I entered the room: not a trace of a dog. Brahms looked a little embarrassed and wiped his eyes with the back of his hand like a child who is ashamed: he must have wept violently, for teardrops hung in his beard and his voice sounded soft and unsteady ... Soon afterwards he was heartily cheerful and in a jesting mood.*

The second glimpse dates from the summer of 1880, which Brahms spent at Ischl, and which also saw the birth of the Academic Festival and Tragic Overtures:

*I suddenly saw a man running from the wood across the meadow towards me; I took him for a farmer. I was afraid I had been trespassing and was already reckoning on all sorts of unpleasant eventualities, when to my joy I recognized Brahms in the supposed farmer. But in what condition – what a sight! Bareheaded and in shirt-sleeves, no waistcoat, no shirt collar, he brandished his hat in one hand, with the other dragged his cast-off coat in the grass behind him, and ran on quickly, as though hunted by an unseen pursuer. Already from far off I heard him snorting and groaning. When he came nearer I saw how the sweat was streaming over his hot cheeks from the hair which hung about his face. His eyes were staring ahead into empty space and shone like those of a beast of prey; he appeared like one possessed. Before I recovered from my shock he had shot past me, so close that we almost collided. I immediately realized it was inadvisable to call to him. He was glowing with creative fire. I shall never forget that harrowing impression of elemental force.*

The musician–critic Richard Specht completes the picture with a reminiscence of Brahms at home in Vienna: 'He might be espied in the small hours of the morning walking in the Prater, with short steps, his hat in hands clasped behind his back, his glance resting far away; he would cross the meadows, blind and deaf to all around him, growling, grunting, groaning, much as he was wont to do, audible as far as the tenth row of listeners, when he played the piano in public.'

Like many creative artists, and all great ones, Brahms possessed, from a very early age, extraordinary powers of concentration – a single-minded focus of attention which comprehensively excluded all extraneous impressions. The Austrian pianist Anton Door experienced this on a visit to Germany in 1855.

*I had hardly been a week in Danzig when I saw great bills in the street announcing the forthcoming concert of Clara Schumann, Joseph Joachim and Johannes Brahms. I at once called on Joachim, who received me with cordiality, and we chatted, as old acquaintances, of home and our experiences. During the whole time we were together, a slender young man with long, fair hair paced continually to and fro in the background smoking cigarettes, without troubling himself in the least about my presence, or even showing by an inclination of the head that he observed me at all; in a word, I was as empty air for him. This was my first meeting with Johannes Brahms.*

*(right) Poster commemorating, among other things, one of the very few occasions at which Brahms's early Sarabande and Gavotte were given a public airing (Danzig, 1855).*

He was to become an energetic champion of Brahms's music. The German-American violinist Arthur Abell, who knew Brahms at the other end of his career, confirms Door's impression: 'If he was talking to someone and another broke in, Brahms would simply not know that the interrupter was there. He'd either give you all he had, or ignore you completely.' At the same time, there were limits even to *his* selective impenetrability. In 1854, from his cramped family quarters in Hamburg, he wrote to Clara, 'How little peace I am given here! ... Even when I manage to find any free time, I have to contend with four people in one room, and with continual runnings in and out.' The overcrowded conditions of his youth may have sharpened his powers of concentration but they likewise intensified his longing for privacy. Many years later, he wrote to Baroness von Heldburg of Meiningen, 'I need complete solitude, not only to achieve my best but even to think of my work at all. This is part of my nature.' Hence his lifelong enthusiasm for walking served a creative as well as a recreational purpose. In his youth it had been his only guarantee of privacy. In manhood it provided a necessary counterpoise to his natural conviviality. He was not cut out to be a hermit. The increasing loneliness of his later years – so critically distinct from solitude – was neither designed nor desired. Although exacerbated by an ironically undisciplined temperament (see Chapter 7), it was perhaps the inevitable loneliness of genius.

For all the talk of 'harrowing' visions, however – of tears, howls, grumbles and struggle – it would be wrong to assume that Brahms's creative life was without its compensating joys. Most truly great artists have been subject to manic-depressive swings without themselves being manic-depressives in any clinical sense. Some have been, of course – Tchaikovsky being a classic case in point, Chopin another, perhaps – but contrary to popular superstition, the dividing line between madness and genius is not necessarily fine. There is no evidence that Monteverdi, Bach, Handel, Schubert and Beethoven were ever mentally ill, much less mad, nor is there in the case of Brahms. But great art encompasses extremes of spiritual experience, and

Mitwoch, den 14. November 1855,

Abends 7 Uhr,

im

# grossen Saale des Schützenhauses.

gegeben von

## Frau Clara Schumann

und den Herren

## Joseph Joachim und Johannes Brahms.

————⋙ ❀❀❀ ⋘————

# PROGRAMM.

## Erster Theil.

1. Sonate von Mozart in Adur für Clavier und Violine, gespielt von Clara Schumann und Joseph Joachim.

2. Fantaisie (op. 77.) von Beethoven, gespielt von Johannes Brahms.

3. Chaconne von Johann Sebastian Bach für Violine allein, gespielt von Joseph Joachim.

## Zweiter Theil.

4. Symphonische Etuden (Etudes en forme de Variations) von Robert Schumann, gespielt von Clara Schumann.

5. Sonate Gdur für Clavier und Violine von Joseph Haydn, gespielt von Johannes Brahms und Joseph Joachim.

6. ⎧ a. Sarabande und Gavotte für Clavier ⎫ gespielt von
   ⎨    von Johannes Brahms,       ⎬ Johannes Brahms.
   ⎩ b Marsch von Fr. Schubert,       ⎭

7. Caprice und Variationen für Violine von Paganini, gespielt von Joseph Joachim.

———————————

Billets à 1 rtl. sind in der Buch- und Musikalien-Handlung von F. A. Weber, Langgasse 78., zu haben. An der Kasse kostet das Billet 1 rtl. 10 sgr.

Wedel'sche Hofbuchdruckerei.

derives much of its energy from emotional friction of one kind or another. Indeed it might defensibly be said that friction is a prerequisite of life.

The young man of twenty-five who wrote disconsolately to Clara Schumann was hardly mad when he wrote to another, 'I am completely in love with music, I adore it; I think of nothing else, or if I do so, it is only if it can heighten the beauty of music for me. Mark my words, I shall be writing love songs again, not now addressed to A or Z, but to music itself!' The zest in Brahms is easily the equal of his melancholy. Albert Dietrich was another who knew him in his twenties, and wrote of him:

*With all his depth, he was fresh and lively and entirely untouched by modern morbidity. His nature was healthy through and through, and even the most sustained mental effort hardly strained it. But then he could fall fast asleep at any time of the day he chose. In his intercourse with those of his own capacity he was lively, sometimes exuberant, rough and full of mad conceits. He would come bounding up my stairs with a youthful impetuosity, knock at the door with both fists and enter like a whirlwind without waiting to be bidden.*

With Joachim, whose sense of humour was never his strongest suit, Brahms adopted a more circumspect tone, but his high spirits were unmistakable:

*I have these days arranged my second Serenade for piano duet. Don't laugh, but it made me feel quite rapturous. I have rarely written down notes with such delight: the sounds penetrated me so lovingly and softly that I became glad through and through. I add in all sincerity that my blissful feelings were by no means enhanced by any thought of myself as creator. But it was ridiculous all the same.*

Even when well short of rapture, the act of composition was often a pleasure to him. To Clara, in 1859: 'Tomorrow my girls are rehearsing a psalm which I've composed for them. I wrote it in the evening a week ago ... and it kept me happy until midnight.' Indeed Joachim remarked to Bettina von Arnim, 'How enviable is a nature like Brahms's, on whom work has the most soothing effect.'

Among the least convincing lines in Joachim's already quoted character sketch (see p. 84) is his assertion that Brahms 'has never once troubled to consider what others, according to their natures and the course of their development, will hold in esteem'. Where his own work was concerned, he considered it almost daily. On the one hand he was principled and uncompromising to a fault, on the other he shared in our universal desire to be appreciated and was almost pathetically needful of encouragement. In 1888, now fifty-five and at the height of his worldwide celebrity, he wrote to Clara, with reference to his latest violin sonata (previously sent to Elisabeth von Herzogenberg, who loved it), 'I never really believe that a new piece of mine could please anyone and this is still true. I still have doubts as to whether you will agree with Frau Herzogenberg's letter. If you don't like the sonata as you read it through, don't play it with Joachim but send it back to me.' And to Billroth, after the première of the First Symphony: 'You cannot imagine how beautiful and heart-warming it is to sense a sympathy like yours. In such a moment one realizes that this is the best part of composing and all that is connected with it.' And to Billroth again, this time on the *Schicksalslied*, 'You cannot believe how important and how precious your favourable comment is to me, and how much I appreciate it.'

Despite the meticulous care which he lavished on them, Brahms's attitude to his own scores and their treatment by his interpreters was sometimes ambivalent, or at any rate ambiguously expressed, as when he wrote to Joachim of the Fourth Symphony:

*I have marked a few tempo modifications in the score with pencil. They may be useful, even necessary, for the first performance. Unfortunately such markings often find their way into print (with me as with others), where, for the most part, they do not belong. Such exaggerations are only necessary when a composition is unfamiliar*

*The diminutive Brahms walking with his friend Klaus Groth, in Thun, 1888. Normally it was Brahms who walked with his arms behind his back.*

*to an orchestra or soloist. In such cases I often cannot do enough pushing or slowing down to produce even approximately the passionate or serene effect I want. Once a work has become a part of one's flesh and blood then in my opinion nothing of that sort is justifiable any more. In fact, the more one deviates from the original, the less artistic the performance becomes. With my older works I frequently find that everything falls into place without much ado and that many marks of the above-mentioned type seem entirely superfluous.*

One aspect of Brahms's own performances, as we have seen (p. 35), was a particularly individual rhythmic freedom which was occasionally perplexing even to his staunchest supporters. It comes, therefore, as no surprise that Brahms had little use for metronome markings: 'For me,' he confessed to Henschel, 'it is an instrument of no value. In my experience, everyone has later repented of the figures he has given out. Those metronome marks which one finds in my compositions I was cozened by good friends into putting there; for myself, I have never believed that my blood and a machine could get on well together.' Here was another thing he shared with Beethoven, who had expressed himself on the same subject, almost verbatim.

# Brahms and the Chorus

If there is any one work which may be said to have marked the biggest turning point in Brahms's career as a composer, that work is the German Requiem, held by many to be his greatest achievement. Certainly nothing else of his combines such scope with such breadth of conception. At roughly an hour and a quarter in performance it is his longest work by a very wide margin, outdistancing its closest competitor, the D minor Piano Concerto, by almost half an hour. Born in a century of rampant nationalism, nowhere more extravagantly demonstrated than in Wagner's *Ring* cycle, its title is easily misleading. There is nothing remotely chauvinistic in the work. Its name derives solely from the fact that the text, drawn from the Bible, is in German rather than the customary Latin, and serves, additionally, to distinguish it from the traditional rites of the Roman Catholic Church. By the time of its completion in 1868, Brahms, brought up as a good north German Protestant, had long since lost his Christian faith. Karl Martin Reinthaler, Kapellmeister of Bremen Cathedral where the work had its first complete performance, was clearly troubled by its lack of any clear doctrinal message. As he wrote to Brahms:

*The central point about which everything turns in the consciousness of the Christian is absent. 'If Christ be not risen then our faith is in vain,' says St Paul. All the same, you say 'Blessed are the dead which lie in the Lord from henceforth,' which can only mean since the accomplishment of Christ's work of redemption.*

*Headquarters of the Gesellschaft der Musikfreunde, whose concert director Brahms became in 1872. Pen and wash by Norbert Bittner.*

To which Brahms replied:

*As regards the title I will confess I should gladly have left out 'German' and substituted 'Human'. Also that I knowingly and intentionally dispensed with passages such as St John's Gospel Ch. 3 Verse 16. ['For God so loved the world, that he gave his only begotten Son, that whosoever believeth in him should not perish, but have everlasting life.'] On the other hand, I have no doubt included much because I am a musician, because I can neither argue away nor strike out a 'henceforth' from my venerable extracts.*

Brahms had been toying with the idea of composing a Requiem in German, based on texts from the Lutheran Bible, ever since 1857, a year after the death of Schumann. Like many of his works, it was a long time in the making. It had its genesis in a funereal, march-like movement, jettisoned from the sonata for two pianos which eventually grew into the D minor Concerto and ultimately reborn as the Requiem's second movement, *Denn alles Fleisches ist wie Gras* (For all flesh is as grass). By 1861, Brahms had found the texts for four additional sections of the Requiem, but it wasn't until 1865, following the death of his mother, that the work got underway in earnest.

From the time of its first complete performance in 1869, when Brahms was thirty-six, it met with near universal enthusiasm and set the seal on his stature as a composer of the front rank. It was neither the first nor the last of his choral endeavours but it brought that branch of his output to a height which he was never to achieve again.

He had begun his choral career, as we've seen (p. 10), in 1847, as a fourteen-year-old city boy summering with the Giesemann family in Winsen. He was subsequently conductor of the Detmold Choral Society (1857), the Hamburg Ladies' Choir (1859), the Vienna Singakademie (1863) and the Vienna Gesellschaft der Musikfreunde (1872), where he had a chorus of three hundred and an already numerous orchestra which he upped to a hundred players. For each of these he composed music, including many unaccompanied part-songs for female, male and mixed voices, three important and predominantly austere groups of motets which demonstrate his formidable contrapuntal powers (almost certainly unparalleled since Bach), folk-song arrangements for four-part choir, and thirteen canons for female voices. With the partial exception of the motets, most of these works are now very seldom performed.

Of the accompanied choral works, apart from the Requiem, only the so-called 'Alto Rhapsody' (whose all-male choir has a very subordinate role) has secured a place anywhere near the centre of the permanent repertoire. Still little known to any but the most committed enthusiasts are the extraordinarily powerful and affecting *Nänie*, op. 82, whose relative neglect is hard to understand, the *Schicksalslied* (Song of Destiny) [CD1; see also p. 151], which is better known, and the fascinatingly scored Part-songs, op. 17, for female voices, two horns and harp. All of these have been recorded and are well worth seeking out.

# CHAPTER 6

# Brahms and Women

*Love bade me welcome, yet my soul drew back.*

George Herbert

*(left) Ethel Smyth in her 20s. This formidable bastion of the feminist movement found the sexist Brahms 'extraordinarily kind and fatherly'. Charcoal sketch by John Singer Sargent.*

Rarely out of love, yet doomed, apparently, to bachelorhood and isolation, Brahms was inspired to many of his greatest achievements, and destined to many of his bitterest disappointments, by his idealization of women. No composer's work is more permeated with the pains and masochistic pleasures of unrequited love (a fact cruelly seized upon by Nietzsche, who impertinently attributed Brahms's inspiration to 'the melancholy of impotence', and dubbed him 'The Musician of the Unsatisfied').

The most abiding influence on his development as a child was not unnaturally his mother, who seems to have been blessed with an equable temperament, and a deep but never oppressive maternal instinct which was extended alike to her children and her husband, who, remember, was seventeen years her junior. Frail and physically disadvantaged (one leg was longer than the other, resulting in a marked limp), she was almost spectacularly plain and had long since resigned herself to spinsterhood when the mercurial Johann Jakob proposed marriage after knowing her for a week. At the time of their wedding she was already forty-one, and they lost no time in starting a family (see p. 4). Although poorly educated, she was a woman of obvious intelligence and exceptional charity. In the one hundred and twenty letters she wrote to Johannes there is scarcely a complaint to be found, about anyone or anything. Sustained by her untrammelled Protestant faith, she gave most of her energies to helping others. 'After all,' she once wrote, 'what should give me greater joy than to help and serve my fellow creatures to the best of my abilities. People who live only for themselves are only half alive.' There is no doubt that she loved all three of her children, but there is equally no doubt that Johannes was the light of her life. Despite the poverty of their circumstances, the Brahms children grew up in a happy home. As it happens, the marriage was later to founder, but for the first thirty-odd years there is no evidence that it was ever anything but harmonious. In his mother, the child Brahms perceived the perfect woman: loving, protective, encouraging and uncomplaining – and compounded of natural common sense. If there was order, peace and a sense of thanksgiving in the Brahms household, it was largely Christiane who provided it. Despite her very limited education, it was she alone in the family who seemed to have an intuitive understanding of Johannes's inner world, and it was consequently with her that he spent most of his free time. His love of her informed the whole of his life. As his childhood friend Louise Japha recalled, 'It went to one's heart when he spoke of his mother, he was so utterly devoted to her.'

It would be difficult to conceive a greater contrast in Brahms's experience of the opposite sex than that between his mother, with her continuous emphasis on the beautiful and the good, and the painted whores of the Hamburg docklands who introduced him to the world of sex, lust and prostitution. It was here, in the beer halls, dancing parlours and 'stimulation saloons' which flourished in and around 'Adulterer's Walk', that the young Brahms first plied his own trade for money, and it left scars that never entirely healed. He himself spoke too little of his experiences to justify the psychoanalytical 'insights' foisted on him by some biographers, but on the rare occasions when he acknowledged this chapter of his life at all, his bitterness was unmistakable: 'They were with the lowest sort of public women – the so-called "Singing Girls" ... And these half-clad girls, to make the men still wilder, used to take me on their laps between dances, kiss and caress and excite me. This was my first impression of the love of women.' That he *was* excited, he seems openly to admit. It is even possible, though not probable, that he lost his virginity to just such a 'singing girl' and that sex remained for him an act of lust, too tainted and besmirched by these associations to serve also as an act of love. It was widely said that he frequented prostitutes throughout his later life, but the theory has seriously been advanced that he suffered lifelong impotence and died a virgin. Whatever the truth, there can be no doubt that his sexual life was highly complex and unsatisfactory. His pupil Robert Kahn stated categorically (though on what authority we do not know) that 'he was very highly sexed', and though he was late to mature physically (at twenty-four he had the beardless cheeks and unbroken voice of a young boy), 'several quite independent informers', writes Florence May, 'have concurred in describing him as being [at eighteen] something less than indifferent to the society of ladies, and especially of young ones'.

His attitudes to women in general were characteristically inconsistent, and their expression was undoubtedly influenced by a certain male chauvinist bravado. Small wonder that they earned the disapproval of that doughty feminist Ethel Smyth, who met him first in 1878. She came to know him well and found him, on the whole, 'extraordinarily kind and fatherly'.

*What angered me, however, were his views on women, which were the views prevalent in Germany, only I had not realized the fact . . . Brahms, as an artist and bachelor, was free to adopt what may be called the poetical variant of the 'Kinder, Kirche, Küche' axiom [children, church, kitchen], namely that women are playthings. He made one or two exceptions, as such men will, and chief among these was Lisl [Elisabeth von Herzogenberg, their mutual friend], to whom his attitude was perfect: reverential, admiring and affectionate, without a tinge of amorousness. It especially melted him that she was such a splendid Hausfrau, and during his visits she was never happier than concocting some exquisite dish to set before the king; like a glorified Frau Röntgen she would come in, flushed with stooping over the range, her golden hair wavier than ever from the heat, and cry 'Begin that movement again; that much you owe me!' and Brahms's worship would flame up in unison with the blaze in the kitchen. He was adorable with Lisl . . . His ways with other womenfolk – or to use the detestable word forever on his lips, 'Weibebilder' – was less admirable. If they did not appeal to him he was incredibly awkward and ungracious; if they were pretty, he had an unpleasant way of leaning back in his chair, pouting out his lips, stroking his moustache, and staring at them as a greedy boy stares at jam tartlets.*

She would not have been amused at Brahms's remark to Joachim with reference to an unidentified female admirer, 'Do not be seduced by the bosom of her dress. She herself hasn't got one.' And though Smyth herself was hardly without humour, she might well have overlooked the fact that Brahms's tongue was firmly in his cheek when he advised Hermann Levi, 'If you need a woman pianist, I can strongly recommend Fräulein Leschetizky, née Essipoff . . . She is as unmusical as all female pianists, but she plays properly and she is a woman you could well bear without a piano.' As it happens, the two most durable loves of Brahms's life, after his mother, were both pianists of exceptional quality. One was Elisabeth von Herzogenberg, as mentioned above; the other, and greater, was Clara Schumann.

*

When we last met Brahms in the Schumann household, he was a disarmingly innocent youth of twenty, on the brink of a lifelong fame. On the day of his arrival, Clara,
fourteen years his senior, had discovered that she was carrying her seventh child,
and Robert, at forty-three, was the very picture of familial contentment and robust
good health. But the picture was deceiving. For more than two decades he had
increasingly been subject to severe, recurrent headaches, dizziness, insomnia, ringing in the ears, sudden and debilitating anxiety attacks and wildly fluctuating
moods. In the weeks prior to Brahms's arrival he had begun to find difficulty in
speaking and was experiencing aural hallucinations. Behind the façade of normality
he had become increasingly dependent on Clara, who was balancing the roles of
principal bread-winner, wife, mother and world-famous pianist with an energy and
inner resourcefulness that beggar belief. On 27 February 1854, hounded by demoni-
acal shriekings in his ears, Schumann threw himself into the Rhine. Rescued before
drowning, he was committed at his own request to an asylum at Endenich near
Bonn, where he remained until his death in 1856. In the intervening months,
Brahms, 'the young eagle', devoted himself almost wholly to the support and suc-
cour of Clara and her young family. Early on in this desperately difficult time, Clara
confided to her diary:

*That good Brahms always shows himself a most sympathetic friend. He does not say
much, but one can see in his face, in his speaking eye, how he grieves with me for
the loved one he so highly reveres. Besides, he is so kind in seizing every opportunity
of cheering me by any means of anything musical. From so young a man I cannot
but be doubly conscious of the sacrifice, for a sacrifice it undoubtedly is for anyone
to be with me now.*

In that, she was mistaken. The young man was deeply in love with her.

We have no evidence, but it seems probable that Brahms fell in love with Clara
more or less on sight. Directly on hearing the news of Schumann's breakdown and
incarceration he rushed to be at her side. In this, he had the heartfelt support of
his mother, who even found money to send him. That the twenty-one-year-old
found himself in a state of some considerable emotional confusion seems clear
from a letter he addressed to Joachim in the spring of that year:

*I believe that I do not have more concern and admiration for her than that I love
her and am under her spell. I often must restrain myself forcibly from just quietly
putting my arms around her and even ... I do not know, it seems to me so natural
that she could not misunderstand. I think I can no longer love an unmarried girl**

---

*Brahms here uses the word *Mädchen* (literally 'maiden', hence virgin).

*– at least, I have quite forgotten about them. They but promise heaven while Clara shows it revealed to us.*

In August, he wrote to one of his Winsen friends, Herr Blume:

*Frau Schumann went with a friend on the 10th of this month to Ostend for the benefit of her health. I, after much persuasion, resolved to make a journey through Swabia in her absence. I did not until now know how greatly I was attached to the Schumanns, how I lived in them; everything seemed barren and empty to me, every day I wished to turn back, and was obliged to travel by rail in order to get quickly to a distance and forget about turning back. It was of no use; I have come as far as Ulm, partly on foot, partly by rail; I am going to return quickly, and would rather wait for Frau Schumann in Düsseldorf than wander about in the dark. When one has found such divine people as Robert and Clara Schumann, one should stick to them and not leave them, and inspire one's self by them.*

In the Schumanns, Brahms encountered people whose experience and sophistication were far beyond his own, a fact which lends added poignancy to the paternalistic attitude evident in certain of his letters to Clara, who was biologically old enough to be his mother. 'My dear Clara,' he writes in 1857, a year or so after Schumann's death,

*You really must try hard to keep your melancholy within bounds and see that it does not last too long. Life is precious and such moods as the one you are in consume us body and soul. Do not imagine that life has little more in store for you ... You must seriously try to alter, my dearest Clara ... Passions are not natural to mankind; they are always exceptions or excrescences. The man in whom they overstep the limits should regard himself as an invalid and seek a medicine for his life and for his health. The ideal and genuine man is calm both in his joy and in his sorrow.*

No sentence in this letter is more striking than Brahms's immaturely mature assertion that 'passions are not natural to mankind'. In what light, then, are we to see not only Schumann and Brahms himself but the entire romantic movement? And with what feelings of guilt and bewilderment must Brahms have written, as he was soon to do,

*My beloved Clara, I wish I might write to you as tenderly as I love you, and do all of the good things for you that I wish you. You are so endlessly dear to me that I cannot express it. I would go on forever calling you 'darling' and all sorts of other things without ever tiring of endearments ... My dearly Beloved, I am a man of straw and far from worthy of being thus locked in your heart, my dear and glorious Clara. But go on doing it, in and to your heart, as I do with you! ... No thought goes*

*from me to you which does not entirely surround you and pay heed to all your cares*
*… I love you more than myself and anyone or anything in the world … Deeply*
*beloved Clara, now the longed-for Sunday, for which I have so fervently been waiting,*
*is finally drawing near. If only it brings you with it! I am actually shivering with*
*expectation. It is becoming harder and harder to get used to being separated*
*from you.*

Elsewhere, he beseeches her, 'What have you done to me? Can you not release me
from this magic?' And again, 'I regret every word I write to you which does not
speak of love. You have taught me and are every day teaching me more and more
to recognize and to marvel at the nature of love, affection, and self-denial … I wish
I could always write to you from my heart, to tell you how deeply I love you, and
can only beg of you to believe it without further proof.' On one occasion he turned
uncharacteristically poetical: 'Thy missive, oh Lady, has dropped balsam into a soul
tormented by longing and desire and brought healing to a torn and ailing heart …
Reason is deranged, and the heart lost. Would to God that I might be allowed this
day to tell thee, rather than to send this letter, that I die from love of thee!'

At other times he was more circumspect, and was forced to acknowledge that
the age gap between them was more than a merely conventional disadvantage:

*You bear your sorrow with such dignity that it is only too easy to forget your pain*
*and to indulge lightly in jests. I am still young, even boyish at times: you must forgive*
*me. You surely believe and know that my feelings are more serious and that youthful*
*exuberance or light-heartedness make me seem different, but can never let me forget.*

And in 1858:

*You take me, I believe, to be quite different from what I am. I am never, or extremely*
*rarely, satisfied with myself. Perhaps never comfortable, but pleased and darkly*
*moody by turns. However, I am so disinclined and unfitted to lament my lack of*
*genius and skill to others that in any case I always present a different appearance.*
*In addition to which I am so happy about the pleasure I give to others, and especially*
*you, that I cannot help showing it and looking as if I appeared so bright and sure of*
*victory thanks to merits of my own. Oh why can we not look into ourselves and know*
*just how much of divinity there be in us?*

That Clara's debt to Brahms was incalculable she freely acknowledged: 'Like a
true friend, he came to share all my sorrow; he strengthened the heart that
threatened to break, he uplifted my mind, brightened my spirits where he could.
He was, in short, my friend in the fullest sense of the word.' But more than a friend?
A diary entry from 1855 sounds rather as though she is trying to convince herself

*The elderly Clara Schumann in 1889, still in her widow's weeds. Oil painting by Richard Scholz.*

otherwise: 'There is the most complete accord between us. It is not his youth that attracts me: not, perhaps, my own flattered vanity. No, it is the fresh mind, the gloriously gifted nature, the noble heart that I love in him.' November 1854 found her in Hamburg, where she met Brahms's parents. Noting the great disparity in their ages she wrote of Johannes in her diary, 'Perhaps I am appointed to be a mother to him in her place.' And in a later entry she comments '. . . for indeed I love him like a son'. There were certainly times, throughout her life, when she behaved towards him like a mother – a fact reflected in numerous little asides as when Brahms, in sending her some songs, added, 'Please don't judge them harshly at first reading ... Forgive me, but I'm just afraid of being scolded.' In another letter to Christiane, however (in 1855, a year or so before Schumann's death), she sounds something more than merely maternal: 'From here, my dear friend, I can send you little or no good news. I am feeling the separation from Johannes too painfully ... He is the dearest friend I have in all the world.'

He was. For all his youth, he had taken over the supportive role once played by Schumann, he afforded her once again the opportunity to stand as midwife to a burgeoning musical genius, he drew out and stimulated her musical imagination as Robert had, he loved and entertained her children, and despite her deficiencies in humour, he made her laugh. He was also sexually attractive. There is no evidence to suggest that they were ever lovers in a physical sense, and the period of their closest association was so fraught with anxiety and grief on Clara's part, and derived so much of its character and energy from the focal point of Schumann's illness, that an overtly sexual relationship between them seems unlikely, even had their deeply entrenched sense of honour allowed it. Nor was it likely that Brahms could then have reconciled his almost obsessively polarized views of sex and love. Clara Schumann represented in every respect his conscious ideal of womanhood. And a part of that ideal was the negation of the baser instincts he had seen at work in the *Animierlokale* of Hamburg.

With Robert's death their relationship reached a watershed. On a holiday in Switzerland, in the company of Brahms's sister and two of Clara's sons, they seem to have decided to go their separate ways, maintaining and nurturing a friendship which was to last for forty years but following their different stars. When and how these decisions were reached in such well-chaperoned circumstances we shall never know, but from that time onwards there was no prospect of any formal union. The likelihood is that the motivating impulse came from Brahms, who had not long since written to Clara, 'You have taught me and are every day teaching me more and more to recognize and to marvel at the nature of love, affection, and self-denial.' That Brahms consciously, and repeatedly, practised self-denial in the service of his art is hardly to be questioned. Nor can one doubt that in almost every case the ostensible sacrifice released him, if only temporarily, from a deep-rooted fear of entrapment by women.

In the autumn, following their return from Switzerland, Clara sold the house in Düsseldorf and moved to Berlin, while Brahms now drifted into a semi-nomadic life, with Hamburg and his family as its base. He had devoted himself body and soul to Clara and her family for the best part of four years, and professionally had little to show for it. Now it was time to set his own course straight. Never again would he unburden himself to anyone as he had to Clara. Never would he feel the same unguarded trust, nor lay himself open to such risk of disappointment and loss. Clara was to remain the greatest love of Brahms's life. But there were others, and sooner than might be expected.

*

In the autumn of 1857, Brahms accepted a minor post at the tiny court of Detmold, where he served as conductor, court pianist and tutor to the young Princess Friederike, whose example led to a stream of wealthy female pupils whose custom and company made up for his very modest salary. For his holiday the following summer, he travelled to Göttingen to join Clara, but found himself unexpectedly distracted by the young Agathe von Siebold, whose voice and natural musicianship were to elicit some of his finest songs. Clara, her maternal instincts in abeyance, was unamused and quickly decamped. Brahms now commuted between Göttingen and Detmold and within a year he and Agathe were secretly engaged. When the matter became public, however, Brahms panicked. From Detmold he addressed to her perhaps the strangest letter of his life. 'I love you! I must see you again! But I cannot wear fetters. Write to me, whether I am to come back, to take you in my arms, to kiss you, to tell you that I love you.' Needless to say, she did nothing of the sort. The engagement was abruptly terminated, and they never saw each other again. Ten years were to pass before Agathe was able to shake off the trauma sufficiently to marry another, and it was only in her old age that she could find it in her heart to forgive Brahms. In her *Errinerungen*, cast in the form of a novel, she wrote, still distancing herself by writing in the third person:

*Her memory of her great love for the young man, of the days of her youth, radiant with poetry and beauty, has never faded ... Over and over again, his immortal work has contributed to her happiness. He, however, strode by on his path to fame, and as he, like every genius, belonged to humanity, she gradually learned to appreciate his wisdom in severing the bonds which had threatened to shackle him. She saw clearly at last that she could never have filled his life with her great love.*

For Brahms, the matter was more easily resolved, although he too felt the pain of it for many years, and acknowledged that he had 'played the scoundrel' with Agathe. Five years later, in 1864, he rather cryptically immortalized her by evoking her name three times in his Second String Sextet with the notes A–G–A–D[ = T]–H–E (in German nomenclature H indicates B natural). 'Here,' he told his friend Gänsbacher, 'I have freed myself from my last love.' In the five years between the break-up and this apparently cathartic sextet, Brahms's solo songs and choral works in particular were almost obsessively concerned with the theme of young women abandoned by their lovers.

After Agathe, Brahms's next significant encounter with the opposite sex was his conductorship of the Hamburg Ladies' Choir, which he founded in 1859 and for whom he wrote a quantity of lovely music. A temporary member was the Viennese Bertha Porubsky, with whom there seems to have been a little innocent dalliance

*The brilliantly gifted Elisabeth von Herzogenberg whose premature death at 44 dealt Brahms a cruel blow. Photograph by Albert Meyer.*

before she returned to Vienna where she soon married and became a mother. They remained good friends, and it was for her first-born that Brahms composed the now famous 'Wiegenlied' (best known simply as 'the Brahms Lullaby') which rapidly became, and has remained, his most popular song.

The most surprising of his romantic attachments, because he never spoke of it to anyone, was a passing infatuation with Julie Schumann, Clara's third daughter, who had grown into a particularly lovely girl by the summer of 1869, during which she and Brahms saw a good deal of one another. No one was more surprised than she, however, by Brahms's reaction to the announcement of her engagement to the Italian Count Victor Radicati di Marmorito. As Clara wrote in her diary, 'On Sunday we told our acquaintances of Julie's engagement. Of course I told Johannes first of all. He seemed not to have expected anything of the sort, and to be quite upset.' And he did nothing to conceal it. Later:

*July 16. I find Johannes quite altered. He seldom comes to the house, and speaks only in monosyllables when he does. And he treats even Julie in the same manner, though he always used to be so especially nice to her. Did he really love her? But he has never thought of marrying, and Julie had never any inclination towards him.*

But if he sulked, it was not altogether in vain. Clara, in her diary again, this time at the end of September:

*A few days ago Johannes showed me a wonderful work for contralto, male chorus and orchestra. It is a long time since I have received so profound an impression; it shook me by the deeply felt grief of its words and music.*

The work was the great Alto Rhapsody, op. 53, on a text from Goethe depicting a solitary man, prey to all the torments of deep loneliness. Brahms's bitterness over Julie's wedding subsided only slowly, and his mood may be gauged by the note he appended to the manuscript of the Rhapsody when he sent it to Simrock, his publisher: 'Here,' he writes, 'I have written a bridal song for the Schumann Countess – but I do this sort of thing only with wrath – with rage!' Yet as he later confessed to his friend Dietrich, he loved the work so much that he placed it under his pillow at night in order to have it near him.

More substantial, and certainly more productive, was Brahms's friendship with Elisabeth von Herzogenberg, a comely, intelligent woman of exceptional musical gifts and remarkable achievements, who became (after Joachim and Clara) the third and last great confidante of Brahms's musical adventures. He consulted her frequently, and often took her advice – an almost unique phenomenon. While not precisely beautiful, she was extraordinarily easy to fall in love with, and many did. Indeed her intense personal magnetism comes through powerfully in her voluminous published correspondence with Brahms, who wrote to her, 'You must know and believe this, that you belong among the few people whom one loves so much that – as your husband is always there to read and hear – one cannot tell you.' He counted her letters to him 'among the most precious memories of my life, and also a rich treasure of temperament and spirit, *which belongs naturally to me alone*' [italics mine]. Her death at forty-four was a grievous blow to him, not lessened by the fact that some mysterious disturbance seems to have clouded their friendship near the end. For many years, hers was the only photograph of a woman to stand on his desk. 'But then,' according to his housekeeper, 'quite suddenly, something troubled their relations. One day it disappeared from the desk, and Brahms casually gave me the frame. "You can put your husband's portrait in this," he said gruffly.'

Elisabeth's death marked the beginning of a series of unexpected losses which only intensified Brahms's growing sense of isolation. In the same year, his sister died, followed some months later by a young woman who had brought nothing but light into the life of the ageing master.

*

In 1883, Brahms made the acquaintance of the young contralto Hermine Spies, whose profound musicality and exceptionally beautiful voice were matched by an ebullient good humour and a girlish charm that Brahms found irresistible. She was equally attracted by him: 'What a really splendid fellow Brahms is! I have been absolutely overwhelmed, enraptured, enchanted, carried away. What a dear he is! In a really happy, youthful, summery mood, he is eternally young.' An unusual picture of the crusty, bewhiskered, old bachelor, but one borne out by the wealth of wonderful songs that now poured from his pen. As his friend Billroth wrote to him, 'If these songs are really new, you must be in the grip of such a strong and wholesome midsummer passion as is in keeping with your healthy and indefatigable nature. I believe there is something behind this. So much the better; one doesn't choose such words and write such songs as these out of the mere habit of composing.' Within four months of their meeting, gossip reached Hamburg that the pair were engaged. Like other similar rumours, before and since, they were unfounded. Hermine did marry, but not for another nine years. In the meantime, she proved to be the first woman who understood Brahms's teasing and sometimes offensive remarks, shrugging them off with good-humoured resilience and being quite ready to give as good as she got. She may also have been the only woman in the whole of his life who enabled him to laugh at himself. Their relationship inevitably diminished in ardour, but they remained friends and her death at the age of thirty-six, less than a year after her wedding, left him stunned.

*Brahms walking in the Ringstrasse, Vienna, with Alice Barbi in 1892. His hat was one of several things that made him a figure of fun where dress was concerned.*

The last of Brahms's serious flirtations was with yet another singer, and another contralto, Alice Barbi.* And from a purely artistic point of view it was not a flirtation but a passion. Brahms wrote of her and spoke about her to his friends in terms of unprecedented enthusiasm. As indeed he spoke to her: 'I had no notion of how beautiful my songs are. If I were young, I would now write love songs.' And he paid her the unique compliment of accompanying the whole of her farewell recital on the eve of her marriage – this at a time when he had generally given up playing in public.

By this time, Brahms himself had long since renounced all thought of marriage, though the reasons he habitually gave can hardly be taken seriously.

*At the time when I might have married a girl, my stuff was being whistled at in the concert hall, or at best received with icy coldness. Now I could bear that perfectly well on my own, since I knew exactly how little it was worth and how the tide would eventually turn ... But if in such moments I had to go back to face a wife, to see her questioning eyes anxiously judging me, and to have to say to her, 'again, nothing' – that I could not have endured.*

*The high-voiced composer's lifelong attraction to low-voiced women seems unlikely to be coincidental.

'At the time when I might have married . . .' What had happened that he should have ruled marriage out thereafter? Was it simply, overwhelmingly, that he had loved and lost in Clara the ideal wife of his dreams and hopes? That no one else could ever live up to her?* Or had he realized from the willing sacrifices of his Schumann years that the commitments of marriage were incompatible with the demands of his own creative imagination, that the spectre of 'fetters' haunted him even before Agathe. Perhaps, despite their youthful differences on the subject, Joachim's motto had been right after all: *'Frei aber einsam'* (Free but lonely).

Brahms had been a solitary child, even in the bosom of his family. From an early age, composition had been his secret world, his refuge, his defence. It was also his vocation, and for all his profound humility, he had a sense of destiny in him long before Schumann's 'Neue Bahnen'. In turning down a prestigious post in Düsseldorf, he defended his decision on unusual grounds: 'In Vienna [where he then lived] one can remain a bachelor without any hindrance. In a smaller city an old bachelor is a caricature. Marriage is something I no longer want – and I do have some reasons to be afraid of the fair sex.' Just what those reasons were, he doesn't say. But one may reasonably wonder whether marriage was ever something he seriously desired. That he often spoke of it is inconclusive. He was naturally chary of the stigma then attaching to bachelorhood, and it is entirely probable that he never really intended to marry Agathe. His continuing preoccupation with the subject of matrimony, however, is evident in such unlikely places as his copy of the Koran, where on page 25 he has cryptically underlined 'Divorce is twice permitted'.

There is no evidence of any kind that Brahms was ever homosexual, but we do know that he generally regarded intimate physical contact as embarrassing if not at times downright abhorrent. Even in portly old age he continued to attract women, but took special pains to keep them, and temptation, at bay. Nor was this only a habit of his later years. At twenty, when a party was arranged for him in Lüneburg, he is said to have begged his hosts not to invite any women: 'It will be so much nicer without them.' In the years of his greatest celebrity he was inundated with letters, requests and invitations from women, most of which he declined, with varying degrees of politeness. 'After fourteen epistles one must finally answer them in some way. And the more furious one is, the more sweetly one writes!' One can only assume that the following curious note successfully forestalled a fifteenth:

---

*Throughout his life she remained his benchmark of musical and moral integrity. Decades after their agreed 'separation', Brahms told his friend Widmann, 'Whenever you write anything, always ask yourself whether a woman like Clara Schumann would look upon it with approbation. If you doubt that, then cross it out.'

*Greatly Respected Fräulein –*

*I should long ago have thanked you for the delicious sequel to our rendezvous in the Prater. But I would have said in answer that one enjoys this sort of thing more with father and mother along, and a few good friends. And only now am I able to enquire whether Wednesday or Thursday of next week would be agreeable to you.*

*Yours very truly,*

*J. Brahms*

His friend Max Friedländer was once visiting Brahms when two very attractive girls were announced by the housekeeper. 'They had evidently come to offer themselves to their idol. I naturally rose to go, but he absolutely forced me to stay, in order to spoil their game.' And the housekeeper herself recalled that 'ladies never stayed long in his rooms, and the door invariably stood ajar so that I might have gone in at any moment'.

But, who knows, perhaps that open door is what kept the ladies coming. And it may have given Brahms the comfort of a certain mutuality. He knew from long experience that what Ovid said of women, that they 'long for what eludes them, and like not what is offered', applied no less to men.

# Brahms and Song

*(left) Brahms coming out of unofficial retirement to partner his beloved Alice Barbi at her farewell recital in Vienna.*

How appropriate it is that Brahms's most famous piece should be a song. His 'Wieg-enlied' ('the Brahms Lullaby') is known and sung by countless mothers who may never even have heard of its composer. It provides a classic instance of the art song become folk-song. Songs were among the opening clutch of his published works (op. 3, whose first song, 'Liebestreu', became an overnight favourite) and but for the eleven Chorale Preludes for organ they would also have marked the end of his creative life (the *Vier ernste Gesänge* – Four Serious Songs – were his penultimate publication). They constitute, too, the only genre to which he regularly turned throughout his career, thus providing a kind of diary of his inner life.

Throughout his career he preferred women singers to men, and lower voices to high (possibly a compensation for the unnaturally high pitch of his own voice, which caused him such embarrassment in early manhood). Most of his songs were conceived with either a contralto or a baritone in mind, rather than a soprano or tenor, and he had a lifelong preference for low-toned instruments, as in the beautiful songs, op. 91, for alto, piano and viola, published in 1884. He wrote some two hundred original solo songs, plus a wealth of vocal duets, quartets and folk-song settings. With the exception of a few whose long-spanned melodies look at first sight like requiring the lungs of a Wagnerian *Heldentenor*, his songs lie well for the voice, but even as a song-writer, and a great one at that, he still thought like an instrumental composer. While he was by no means insensitive to the texts he set, he was

*Manuscript title page of Brahms's most famous piece – the 'Wiegenlied' or 'Lullaby' – known to millions who may not know any more about Brahms than his name.*

more responsive to their mood and meaning than to the musical or poetic properties of the words themselves. Far more than with, say, Schumann or Wolf, one could entrust many of them to a violinist, a clarinettist or a cellist with only minimal loss to the total artistic experience. Indeed one can put the proposition to the test by comparing the beautiful 'Immer leiser wird mein Schlummer' with the cello tune in the slow movement of the Second Piano Concerto, or 'Regenlied' and 'Nachklang' from op. 59 with the G major Violin Sonata. In the former case, too, we can see the characteristically Brahmsian precedence of musical expression over fidelity to textual niceties. If accenting a weak syllable in the text gets the more telling musical result, Brahms will accent it, however little sense it may make in purely linguistic terms. Schumann or Wolf would never have countenanced such a thing. In some ways Brahms the song-writer is closer to Schubert than to his beloved Schumann. Among other features they share is a marked preference for strophic forms, in which successive verses are set to the same tune. Of the exceptions in Brahms's case, most are in simple ternary, A–B–A form, which means, among other things, that one stanza in every four has to be dropped in order to fit the musical scheme. Time and again, Brahms's accompaniments are conceived for their purely musical and formal effect rather than as specific illustrations of the text. His fidelity to the mood and the meaning of the verse, however, is often extraordinarily acute. It would be an exaggeration to say that one could almost reconstruct the verse on the basis of Brahms's accompaniment alone, but there are times when his profound sympathy with the emotional or spiritual nature of the poem makes it seem that way. It's no accident, nor is it any indication of a lack of literary culture on his part, that Brahms drew predominantly on second- and third-rate poets for his texts. He was a musician, first, last and always, and looked with suspicion on anything that might distract from the essence of the music itself. One of his principal objections to Lisztian programme music and the grand synthesis of the arts championed by Wagner (the ideal of the so-called *Gesamtkunstwerk*) was the risk, as he saw it, of music's being reduced to the status of handmaiden. This was also a factor in his avoidance of opera, the only one of the major musical genres to which he contributed nothing. Since opera is in purely musical terms song writ large this might be an apt time to consider Brahms's attitudes toward it. It was certainly not a subject in which he had no interest, nor one of which he was ignorant.

As Widmann recalled:

*He was always particularly animated when speaking of matters connected with the theatre, as for instance when he once very decidedly demonstrated to me the vaudeville character of the first act of* Fidelio, *which generally passes for a very good textbook. He possessed a genuine dramatic perception, and it gave him real pleasure to analyse the merits and defects of a dramatic subject.*

*Title page of the* Ausgewählte Lieder, *selected songs by Brahms brought out by the Berlin publisher N. Simrock in 1889. Lithograph by Max Klinger.*

And his junior colleague Heuberger remembered a similar occasion:

*We sat together for one whole evening and I remember that Brahms spoke in the greatest detail of Mozart's* Figaro, *laying great stress on the unparalleled manner in which Mozart has overcome the enormous difficulties of his text: 'Mozart,' he remarked, 'has composed it, not as a mere ordinary textbook, but as a complete well-organized comedy.'*

With Kalbeck, too, Brahms repeatedly discussed subjects for operas, as he did with other literary members of his circle. Although he would jokingly declare that he regarded opera as he did marriage and was no longer inclined to risk either, there seems little doubt that he would have liked to try his hand at it if only he could have come up with a suitable libretto.

# CHAPTER 7

# Brahms and Friendship

*I am accustomed to taking friendships very seriously and very simply.*
Brahms to Julius Allgeyer

That he took his friendships seriously is beyond doubt. That they were ever simple is harder to believe. Friendship with Brahms came at a price, and it says much for him and for those who loved him that so many were ready to pay it. So solitary had he been in his youth that it was not until the age of twenty that he formed the kinds of friendship that last a lifetime. Joachim came first, as we've seen. Then came the Schumanns. Many years later, after Robert's death in the asylum at Endenich, Brahms wrote to his friend Julius Otto Grimm: 'To me Schumann's memory is holy. The noble, pure artist forever remains my ideal. I will hardly be privileged ever to love a better person; neither, it is to be hoped, will I ever again have to come so horrifyingly close to such a terrible fate and share such suffering.' During the years of Robert's incarceration, while Clara dauntlessly undertook concert tours to keep the money coming in, the young Johannes stood *in loco parentis*, helping the servants look after the children, of whom there were seven, assuming responsibility for all the family finances (rent, school fees, servants' wages, taxes, investments and so on), and earning a little himself by taking over some of Clara's pupils and acquiring a few of his own. No one appreciated his devotion more than Eugenie, the third daughter.

*I liked to look at Brahms when he said, 'Your mother'. The blue of his eyes showed at its purest and softest. We children loved in Brahms his fresh, youthful virility, his thoroughly German characteristics, his genuineness and reliability, the clarity of his mind which saw and made others see things as they were. But above all we loved him for his love of our mother. Whatever else I have come to doubt in the course of my life, I have never doubted Brahms's loyalty. And if to him her great heart was the strongest attraction, she too knew that her friend had a heart that understood every emotion of hers and would be devoted to her to the end of her days.*

A Brahmsfest at Johann Strauss's in 1894, Brahms appearing less unkempt than usual. Strauss is at the piano. Photogravure by J. Blechinger after oil painting by Franz von Bayros.

On top of all his domestic and pastoral activities, Brahms still found time for composition and strove continually to fulfil Schumann's gargantuan expectations of him (compositions of the period include the Variations on a Theme of Schumann, op. 9, the four Ballades, op. 10, and most importantly of all, a major sonata for two pianos, which was then recast as a symphony before finally emerging as the great D minor Piano Concerto we know today). The friendship with Schumann himself did not cease with his incarceration, nor was the incarceration absolute. Brahms visited him repeatedly, occasionally taking him on walks beyond the confines of

the asylum. There was also a lively correspondence between them, and though Schumann never asked either to see or to hear of his wife (naturally to her extreme distress), Brahms kept him well informed, never, apparently, dreaming that his reports might provoke even the slightest pangs of jealousy on Schumann's part.

In December 1854 we find him writing from Düsseldorf: 'I returned here the evening before Christmas; how long the separation from your wife seemed to me! I had become so accustomed to her inspiring company, I had lived near her so delightfully all the summer and learned to admire and love her so much that everything seemed flat to me, and I could only long to see her again ... I must thank you most warmly for a pleasant word in your last letter, for the affectionate "thou" [Brahms refers here to the informal use of the German pronoun 'Du' as opposed to the formal 'Sie']; your kind wife also makes me happy now by using the same nice, intimate word. It is the highest proof to me of her favour. I will try always to deserve it more.' And later: 'The day was altogether such a delightful one as one does not often experience. Your dear wife understands how to give happiness. You, however, know this better than anyone.'

It should be borne in mind that the incurability of Schumann's illness was by no means taken for granted during the earlier part of his confinement, and he enjoyed periods of lucidity during which he seemed much like his old self. He had a piano in his room, on which Brahms would play for him and at which the two joined forces for the occasional duet. In February 1855, Schumann was allowed out, as Johannes reported to Clara: 'It was very fine to see the heavy doors, which are usually bolted, opened for us ... He was very pleased with my Hungarian hat, just as he used to be in the old days ... So we went to the cathedral, and to the Beethoven monument, after which I brought him back to the road.'

When not visiting or writing to Schumann, Brahms consulted with doctors and visited other institutions which might offer superior treatment. The search proved vain, but it left him with a lifelong horror of mental illness, not lessened by the spectacle of Schumann's own deteriorating condition. By April 1856, it was clear to everyone that Schumann was beyond retrieval. On one particularly distressing visit, he seemed unable to understand a word Brahms spoke, but talked incessantly, apparently to himself, and mostly in an incoherent babble. On 27 July it was clear that the end was not far off, and Clara had her first sight of him since the day of his committal in March 1854. Brahms was there and reported the scene to a friend. 'He lay for some time with closed eyes, and she knelt before him with greater calmness than one would have thought possible. But later on, he recognized her, and he did so again the next day. Once he clearly wished to embrace her and flung his arms around her. Of course, he was past being able to talk any more, one could only make out single words, perhaps in imagination. But even that was bound to make her happy.' Later she despatched a note to Joachim: 'I saw him yesterday. Let me be silent about my own despair, but I did perceive a few loving glances; I shall carry them with me all my life! Pray God he may have a peaceful end. It cannot last much longer.' And Brahms continued: 'I am writing this just in case you wish to see him once more. I would like to add, however, that you must think it over carefully; it is a very, very horrifying and pitiful sight. Schumann is very thin, and there can be no question of conversation or even consciousness.' Joachim came at once. On the 29th, Clara and Johannes went to meet him at the station. When they returned to the asylum Schumann was dead. His funeral followed two days later. As Clara noted in her diary that evening: 'His dearest friends went in front, I came, unnoticed, behind, and it was best that way. All happiness has gone with his passing. A new life begins for me now.'

A new life was shortly to begin for Brahms too: a life of dogged independence, spectacular failures and triumphant successes – and a life in which he was to affect others as Schumann had affected him. Albert Dietrich, for instance, had warmed to him at once in 1853 and found that he only improved on further acquaintance. But Dietrich's tastes were not shared by everyone. As he wrote to his wife in 1862:

*The longer I am with Brahms, the more my affection and esteem for him increase. His nature is equally lovable, cheerful and profound. He often teases the ladies, certainly, by making jokes with a serious air, which are frequently taken in earnest, especially by Frau Schumann. This leads to comical and frequently dangerous arguments, in which I act as mediator, for Brahms is fond of strengthening such misunderstandings, in order to have the last laugh. This to me attractive trait is, I think, the reason why he is so often misunderstood.*

Its attraction for Dietrich suggests that he himself was not often on the receiving end. Clara, on the other hand (as Dietrich implies), was. But this was the least of the strains affecting her friendship with Brahms in the long years after Robert's death. Even a cursory glance at her surviving letters to him reveals that Brahms's characteristic rejection of her advice after pleading for 'the severest criticism' frequently exasperated her. 'Only a mincing little pedant would think of such a thing,' she rebuked him on one such occasion. 'You really are a regular good-for-nothing; first one is to say all that one thinks, and then if one does, one gets one's knuckles rapped.' Nor were expressions of praise and enthusiasm free of danger. In 1857 she writes: 'I'm sorry I didn't write to you about the Hungarian Dances, for you know how I like to please you. I only refrained because I feared you might say something unkind to me, as you have so often done in similar cases before.' And later we find her protesting, 'But I like all the songs [op. 19]. Leave me my joy in them and do not spoil it by your customary remarks.'

*(right) Albert Dietrich in later life. A devoted friend from earliest manhood, he introduced many of Brahms's works to the public as music director at the court of Oldenburg from 1861.*

While Brahms repeatedly stressed the value to him of praise and encouragement, he just as frequently failed to provide it when others were in need of it, as in 1861, when Clara introduced his great 'Handel' Variations to Hamburg: 'I was in agonies of nervousness,' she writes,

*but I played them well all the same, and they were much applauded. Johannes, however, hurt me very much by his indifference. He declared that he could no longer bear to hear the variations, it was altogether dreadful to him to listen to anything of his own and to have to sit by and do nothing. Although I can well understand this feeling I cannot help finding it hard when one has devoted all one's powers to a work, and the composer himself hasn't a kind word for it.*

On another, much later occasion she confides to her diary: 'Brahms comes today. How anxious I feel at heart! If only we could frankly discuss all that has happened, but he gets so violent that one is reduced to silence.' Yet the friendship remained and in some senses deepened throughout her life, and her death was something from which Brahms never really recovered. In her memoirs, Clara's daughter Eugenie has interesting things to say about their long and often difficult relationship.

*The cause of their differences lay in Brahms's uncompromising manner and my mother's extreme sensitivity, which would sometimes see things out of proportion. She had had love lavished upon her all her life, and her soft, affectionate heart could not bear unkind words or blunt manner from those she loved.*

*It is difficult to decide how much of Brahms's brusqueness was natural disposition, or how far life had developed it in him. It is certain that my mother and other friends had been made to feel it even in the early Düsseldorf days, and it comes out occasionally in the first letters to my mother. But on the other hand, these give proof of so warm a heart, so much tender sympathy, that one cannot but ascribe to outward circumstances the callousness with which he could wound his friends' feelings. His genius, the bent of his nature, were in striking contrast to the environment into which he was born. He himself told my mother that as a mere boy he saw things and received impressions which left a deep shadow on his mind.*

*

*Her own mind and heart were laid down on such clear and simple lines that she could not enter into the more complex processes of the human soul. She remained towards Brahms what she had always been. She loved him truly and wholeheartedly. Her feelings for him might have been those of a mother for her son, if admiration had not so strongly predominated. The admiration she felt for the artist was also bestowed on the man. She could as little think of Brahms the man and Brahms the*

*artist as separate entities as she could separate the woman from the artist in herself.*
*She certainly was right! If only she had been able to understand the man as well as*
*she understood the artist! She could see the ruggedness in his compositions, especially*
*the earlier ones, without losing her admiration for the work thereby; but when the*
*ruggedness of his nature came out in his manner, it hurt her deeply.*

In this she was hardly alone. But she was spared Brahms's worst excesses, as when, at a public function, he loudly described the wife of his concert manager as 'an emetic'. On another occasion, at a banquet attended by his then very highly esteemed colleague Hiller, he endured the formal toasting of several prominent contemporary musicians before rising to his feet, proclaiming, 'Now, having drunk to so many living composers, let us drink to a dead one! I lift my glass to Ferdinand Hiller.' Far worse than these, however, was an incident related by the distinguished baritone Max Friedländer:

*In the eighties, I dined with Brahms on his birthday at the house of one of his most*
*intimate Viennese friends, a man whose charming wife and two half-grown children*
*made up the party. Unfortunately, French champagne was served before table. This*
*tasted so good that three bottles were served to the six of us. And at dinner we had*
*some rather strong red wine. Brahms grew more and more silent, but nobody noticed*
*anything curious about him. The talk turned on a beloved woman whom we all*
*knew. Still, the Master was silent – until someone pressed him for his opinion. That*
*was a moment I shall never forget! Abruptly his harsh voice broke into a horrible,*
*coarse tirade against this lady, broadening out to include women in general, and*
*ended by applying to them all a word so vile that I have never been able to repeat*
*it, even to my wife. Then Brahms fell back into his drunken silence. Of course this*
*tirade had burst upon us like a gas-bomb. Our embarrassment was appalling. I*
*remember that the host began a constrained conversation with me about the theatre,*
*to which I replied wholly at random. As soon as we rose from table I went up to our*
*hostess and blurted out that I would go now. But she looked frightened, and begged*
*me: 'For God's sake don't leave us alone with him!' So I stayed.*

And Friedländer's wife recalled, 'When I first met Brahms, I was embarrassed. Scarcely realizing what I was saying, I remarked on the discrepancy between my husband's long acquaintance with him and my own short one. "I only wish," Brahms barked at us, "that it had been the other way around!" Even in paying compliments he could not help his sarcastic, mischievous, biting tone.' A similar failing characterized one of the closest friends of Brahms's later years. 'My unpopularity is unbounded, and I rejoice in it!' Thus the great pianist and conductor Hans von Bülow in early manhood. The two of them together must have been lethal.

*(left) The despotic Hans von Bülow, in his time a friend and champion of Liszt, Wagner and Brahms. Not many could claim that. Pastel drawing by Franz von Lenbach.*

Bülow was first a pupil and then the son-in-law of Liszt, and one of the most ardent champions of Wagner (who later stole his wife). His defection to the Brahmsian camp came relatively late in his career but his zeal was as boundless as his lack of popularity. No great musician felt the influence and power of Brahms more acutely than Bülow, who wrote to his fiancée in 1888:

*You know what I think of Brahms: after Bach and Beethoven he is the greatest, the most exalted of all composers. I consider his friendship my most priceless possession, second only to your love. It represents a climax in my life, a moral conquest. I do not believe that a single musical heart, not even that of Joachim, feels so profoundly or is so deeply immersed in the very depths of his soul as mine.*

Another great musician powerfully affected by Brahms was the conductor Hermann Levi, best remembered today as an ardent champion of Wagner. In 1864, when he was twenty-five and Brahms thirty-one, Levi wrote to Clara: 'Brahms's departure [from Karlsruhe] left me with a sense of emptiness which I have tried in vain to counteract by hard work ... The close contact with Johannes was, I believe, of such profound and lasting influence that nothing else in my musical career can match it. He is for me the very image of the really pure artist and human being.' It might almost be Brahms talking about Schumann. Three years later, Levi's admiration seems only to have intensified: 'Now here is a man! All descendants of Adam generally bear the stamp of their time and its weaknesses on their foreheads; he alone knows how to free himself of all earthly entanglements [!], to remain uncontaminated by the filth and misery of life, and to soar to ideal heights where we can only follow him with our eyes but not join him. Are we to be blamed for being dazzled?' Such adulation is generally doomed to disillusionment, and so it was here. As early as 1867, before serious differences had arisen between them, Levi wrote: 'I fear that Brahms, the man as well as the musician, is now at a crossroads, and one path will lead him to destruction. If he should not succeed in snatching his better self from the demon of abruptness, of coldness, and of heartlessness, then he is lost to us and to his music, for only an all-engendering love can create works of art.'

Whatever his shortcomings in society, Brahms, like his mother, derived the most profound satisfaction from helping others, anonymously whenever possible. Nor was his prodigal generosity confined to friends; it was extended as well to total strangers who struck him as needy and worthy of help. He would frequently part with vast sums and never give the matter a second thought. He himself, however, was exceptionally frugal, spending hardly as much as the interest accruing to his very considerable income. As Richard Specht recalled:

*He could be fiercely annoyed on hearing that one of his acquaintances was in a bad way and I myself heard him say angrily 'Why do people not come to me? I've got plenty!' He would not hear of gratitude and could be exceedingly vexed if anyone whom he had treated so magnanimously began to make words instead of just 'cordially and simply' agreeing. He always behaved as if it were he who was under an obligation. What he secretly gave to young musicians exceeded any scholarship, and many owed him the possibility of their artistic careers.*

No one was more consistently resistant to his generosity than Clara Schumann, and even as early as 1861, when he was not yet thirty, it roused him to a fine anger:

*In all things that concern me you have always treated me, and always will, as though I belonged to you, and yet in all things that concern you I am allowed to do nothing. If I had not a farthing, I should live with you. If I had a house you would certainly live with me. But now I have a purse full ... which I am not allowed to spend ... I can assure you I shall really be furious if you refuse to be my guest [Brahms had invited her to spend a week in Hamburg with her daughter Julie, resting and relaxing at his expense] ... I shall throw all my money out of the window within a month. For what is the good of the trash otherwise?*

Almost thirty years on, nothing had changed, although Clara, now in her seventieth year, was in genuine difficulties: 'It angers me that you have these financial worries – while I swim in money without even noticing it and without having any pleasure because of it. I cannot live otherwise, don't want to, and will not ... and where my heart demands it, I can be helpful – and do good without having to be aware of it. After my death, however, I won't have any responsibilities or special wishes.' And if she wouldn't accept his help for her own sake, he invited her to do it for his own. 'Just think what a great pleasure it would give me if you were simply and nicely to say "yes".'

Financial largesse, however, was among the least of Brahms's contributions to friendship, at least as experienced by himself. He took a childlike joy in sharing the abundant enthusiasms that never left him. Today, the picture postcard message 'Wish you were here' has become a cliché of insincerity, dispensed by millions who wish no such thing. But when Brahms said it, he meant it – as when writing to Clara from his beloved Italy in 1881:

*How often do I not think of you, and wish that your eyes and heart might know the delight which the eye and heart experience here! If you stood for only one hour in front of the façade of the Siena cathedral you would be beside yourself with joy and agree that this alone made the journey worthwhile ... On the following day, at Orvieto, you would be found to acknowledge that its cathedral is even more beautiful, and after all this to plunge into Rome is a joy beyond words ... You can have no conception of how beautiful it is, and you have only to take a little trouble to enjoy it in comfort. Next year you must see that you are free at the end of March, when I shall be able to be with you on the whole of the journey.*

Sadly, as by now he may have come to expect, she declined.

Brahms's passionate enthusiasms were a delight to his friends, but often at some cost to themselves. As Widmann recalled, 'His weekend visits were high festivals and times of rejoicing for me and my family. Days of rest they certainly were not, for the constantly active mind of our guest demanded similar wakefulness from all his associates and one had to pull one's self together vigorously to keep fresh on the plane of his inexhaustible vitality.'

So much is made of Brahms's need for solitude, and of the ever more heart-clutching loneliness expressed in some of his finest music (especially the songs), that we easily overlook his sheer irrepressible conviviality. In 1894, when Brahms was sixty-one, Georg Henschel and his wife travelled to Vienna for the express purpose of spending a few days with him.

*The 'Brahms Room' at the Red Hedgehog, where he consumed much food and drink and enjoyed many convivial hours with friends old and new. Drawing by J. Hackler, 1907.*

*On our arrival, rather late in the evening, we found a note awaiting us at our hotel: 'If not too tired after your journey, do come to us, quite close by, at the restaurant of the Musikverein; just as you are, informally, in your travelling clothes.' Who could resist the temptation? Arrived at the indicated place, we found a little party of men*

Johann Brahms-Zimmer
beim ehemaligen „roten Igel" in Wien.

*Brahms among friends. Hanslick is on Brahms's right, Mühlfeld on his left. Photographed at the home of Viktor von Miller zu Aichholz in Vienna, May 1894.*

*and women, mostly members of the Musikverein, gathered together in a social way as usual after one of their weekly concerts. Brahms, surrounded as always on such occasions by a host of admiring ladies, young and elderly (in regard to those charms and homage his susceptibilities had not by any means lessened with the advancing years), was in excellent spirits and gave us a most cordial welcome ... Early the following morning we went to his rooms. He received us, as was his wont with friends, irrespective of sex, attired in a short jacket of which the lowest button only was put to its proper use; without waistcoat or shirt collar, and in slippers. The coffee-machine – he always made his own coffee in the morning – was still standing on the table; the air of the large yet cosy room was filled with the delicious fragrance peculiar to Viennese coffee; the sun shone brightly through the large windows and the whole atmosphere was one of quiet, inward happiness, contentment and ease.*

How difficult it is to reconcile this picture with Brahms's bitter remark to Rudolf von der Leyen at roughly the same period: 'Those who meet me in company, where I seem contented and ready to jest with others, must think me cheerful: to you I need hardly say that within myself I never laugh.' Or his equally late and still bitterer declaration to Eugenie Schumann: 'I have no friends; if anyone tells you he is my friend, don't believe him!' More likely, Brahms in his darker moments believed that he himself was unworthy of love, and that he, had he received the treatment meted out by him to others, would be incapable of loving those who so abused him. In this mood, his friends' protestations of affection would have a lacerating effect, serving only to heighten his self-dislike, which is seldom far removed from self-pity.

\*

In the days before the telephone, letter-writing was an all but indispensable art for anyone wanting to sustain a friendship, and Brahms applied himself more diligently to this than to many other social skills, though he never pretended to enjoy it. 'I am passionately fond of reading letters from wise, good and dear people,' he once confessed, 'I even have a secret passion for writing letters myself – but it is very secret indeed and completely evaporates in front of notepaper. Never in my life have I written a letter easily or comfortably.' Small wonder, then, that he welcomed the advent of the postcard with vehement ardour. It was a medium he used with characteristic originality when he addressed a simple message to the two Fellinger brothers but spread over two cards, thus:

*Joachim looking ever more professional with advancing years. Not a man you'd want to cross. Cartoon by Spy* (Vanity Fair, *January 1905).*

|                                  |                                  |
|----------------------------------|----------------------------------|
|                                  | San Marino, 12.5.88              |
| Magnificent                      | weather!                         |
| Glorious                         | journey!                         |
| Best                             | greetings!                       |
| to father                        | and mother                       |
| and everything possi-            | ble and impossible               |
| from one who heartily            | remembers you all                |
|                                  | J.B.                             |

In 1881, Brahms had written a letter which was to have a more far-reaching effect on his personal life than he had the foresight to imagine at the time. His oldest friend, Joachim, became obsessed with the idea that his wife (almost certainly blameless) had been unfaithful to him. Brahms sided with the wife and wrote to her at length in support of her claim to innocence, saying many harsh things about her husband. When Joachim sued for divorce, this letter, to Brahms's horror and his friend's shocked disbelief, was produced in evidence by the defence, thereby assuring at a stroke Joachim's defeat in court and the instant demise of his friendship with Brahms. It is a measure of his artistic integrity that he continued to champion Brahms's music with undiminished vigour (as he told a friend, 'artist and man are two different things . . . I can do no other than feel this music with my whole being . . . it works on me like a force of Nature'.) The rift was eventually healed, with the composition of the Double Concerto (Brahms's last orchestral work) in 1887, but the close friendship of their earlier years had been irretrievably damaged.

The sad fact is that not one of Brahms's friendships remained unclouded, and while he accepted some measure of the blame he seemed unable to restrain his inner demon. In 1892, on her seventy-third birthday, he wrote to Clara (from whom he had for various reasons become largely estranged), 'In my dealings with my friends I am aware of only one fault – my lack of tact.' Only one? And lack of tact? He had by that time become notorious, far beyond Vienna, for his apparently compulsive rudeness, his sudden, violent tantrums at dinner parties or in the street, his malicious and often cruel wit, and an apparently chronic inability to apologize. As with so many lonely people, his increasing isolation was largely self-earned. Yet for the most part he retained his charm, his generosity of purse and spirit, and his boundless energy. That he was subject to bouts of extreme inner turmoil, born in part from his obsessive sense of privacy, was obvious to most, and his worst excesses were generally soon forgiven. While he would probably have agreed with Samuel Butler that 'friendship is like money, easier made than kept', it was his lifelong privilege to have done both in almost equal measure.

# Brahms and Chamber Music

Nothing in Brahms is more captivating, more exciting, more vivid or more varied than his chamber music. His seven duo sonatas, seven trios, six quartets, five quintets and two sextets have all enjoyed uninterrupted favour at the centre of the concert repertory from the moment they were published. So too has the lone Scherzo for Violin and Piano on CD1 (for further comment see p. 149) – and with very few gaps they represent him at every stage of his creative career.

Chamber music has aptly been dubbed by one commentator 'the music of friends'. On those grounds alone the naturally convivial Brahms would have been attracted to it. His chamber works are all in the nature of conversations, leavened with occasional argument but with the unique advantage that in music several voices may speak at once with no loss of clarity, cohesion or responsiveness. With its definitive restriction of one instrument per part it is also an ideal medium for a composer of Brahms's contrapuntal leanings. The interweaving of discrete melodic strands is perhaps the single most illuminating feature of Brahms's style, for player and listener alike. One has only to cultivate the ability to hear horizontally, as it were, to listen in terms of melody (or of *concurrent* melodies) rather than in harmonic blocks, and all the stodginess so long and so wrongly attributed to Brahms's textures disappears in favour of a radiant, often ravishing sonority. Partly for this reason, the most popular of Brahms's chamber works have always been those which combine the greatest variety of instrumental colours: the Piano Trios (piano, violin

and cello), the Horn Trio (horn, violin and piano), the Clarinet Trio (clarinet, cello and piano), the three Piano Quartets (piano and string trio) and the great F minor Piano Quintet have all won greater favour with musicians and the public than the three quartets and two quintets for strings alone. The two meltingly beautiful String Sextets (a medium invented by Brahms) have fared better, partly because of the sheer luminosity of sound, partly because they contain, especially in the case of the first, in B flat, some of the most sensuous music he ever wrote. His own piano arrangement of the variations from the First Sextet perfectly demonstrates the extent to which the substance of the music transcends the ancillary effects of instrumental colour.

In most of the works with piano, Brahms's keyboard writing is of an immensity and richness almost orchestral in effect and seldom if ever encountered in chamber music before. And from the beginning, he thought big. His first published chamber work, the B major Piano Trio of 1854, is of a symphonic size and scope which may be gauged by the fact that when he came to revise the work almost forty years later he cut it by some 499 bars. It is this revised version that we normally hear today. Still bigger, in almost every sense, is the magnificent F minor Piano Quintet, op. 34. Like the D minor Concerto, it had an adventuresome genesis, starting life as a string

*Hofstetten, on Lake Thun in Switzerland, where Brahms spent three consecutive summers 1886–8. Watercolour by R. Dickenmann.*

quintet with two cellos (as in Schubert's great C major Quintet), reappearing as a sonata for two pianos (op. 34b), in which form one still hears it occasionally today, before reaching its present form in 1864. In its rhapsodic sweep, its electrifying intensity and drive, and its epic dramatic pacing (just try and beat the cumulative momentum of the Finale), it makes a superb introduction to Brahms's chamber music, as does the shorter and less imposing Horn Trio, op. 40. This brilliant exercise in unusual tone colours is equally unusual in design. Beginning with a ruminative Andante in rondo form, it continues with a tremendously exhilarating Scherzo, vividly reminding us in its style and spirit that the horn was originally an outdoors instrument. The sombre Adagio that follows is one of the darkest, most profoundly moving meditations Brahms ever wrote (clearly reflecting the recent death of his mother, to whom he was exceptionally close). Very unusually for Brahms, the irresistibly exuberant Finale is the only movement cast in traditional sonata form.

Another of Brahms's most sure-fire hits is the large-scale Piano Quartet no. 1 in G minor (later orchestrated by Schoenberg, partly by way of demonstrating its truly symphonic character). The almost extravagantly gypsyish Finale is perhaps the most colourful, exciting and virtuosic of all Brahms's 'Hungarian Dances', though in this case he doesn't give it that name. The Second Quartet also has its gypsy elements, again in the Finale, but on the whole this is a gentler, more autumnal work. The third and last of the Piano Quartets, the C minor, is an altogether different affair, sombre, sometimes almost sinister, terse, troubled, and sprung with nervous energy of a near tragic kind. When sending the manuscript to his publisher Simrock, Brahms wrote, 'You may place a picture on the title page, namely, a head with a pistol in front of it. This will give some idea of the music. I shall send you a photograph of myself for the purpose!' Such gloom and melodrama as this are rare in Brahms's music. Nor, for all the quasi-orchestral piano writing, is his chamber music predominantly bold and gestural. Its moments of intimacy are many, and in the case of the G major Violin Sonata, he only half-jokingly remarked, 'Here even one listener is too many.' The same could hardly be said of the two sonatas for cello and piano, whose lyrical breadth, rhetorical flair and textural felicities have recommended them to every generation. In a survey as necessarily brief as this it is impossible to discuss every work, but it should be stressed that any reasonably extensive exploration of Brahms's chamber music will show up for the calumny it is the knee-jerk assertion that Brahms was insensitive to instrumental colour.

# CHAPTER 8

# Brahms and History

*I am a poor recluse, who really feels much more comfortable when the world takes no notice of him.*

Brahms in a letter to Hans von Bülow, January 1890

*(left) A rare glimpse of Brahms with his spectacles – a drawing by Willy von Beckerath, 1896.*

Brahms was one of the purest musicians who ever lived. To put it coldly, he believed that the elements of music – pitch, duration, volume, tone colour, texture and form – are entirely sufficient to its purposes. That is to say, among other things, that music can reflect and express the most profound spiritual and emotional experiences without recourse to external references. He also had the born classicist's belief in the expressive and aesthetic properties of form itself. Unlike many masters in, say, the French tradition, he valued craftsmanship, which he prized to an unsurpassed degree, primarily as a means to an end – and more precisely, to a specifically expressive end. We have only to remember his question to Joachim – but is it good *music*? (p. 81) – to be reassured on that point. He was constitutionally suspicious of any music that relied for its full effect on external references, with the important exception of word-settings: as one of the greatest and most prolific composers of songs and choral works he was hardly in a position to be an unyielding absolutist here. Nor, especially in his songs, can he be entirely exonerated from the charge of writing illustrative music. What he deeply abhorred, however, was the concept of programmatic instrumental music, as exemplified by Liszt's 'invention' of the so-called Symphonic Poem. He likewise deplored the quasi-improvisatory forms resulting from too literal an adherence to the dictates of whatever play, poem, statue, painting or historical event was being represented. For Brahms, music succeeded on the basis of its own inner logic or not at all. His abiding mentors were Bach, Mozart, Haydn, Beethoven and Schubert, and he was readier than most to recognize the true stature of Mendelssohn, 'a great master before whom we should take off our hats! ... would give all my compositions if I could have written such a piece as the "Hebrides" Overture!' Nothing so very bad in that. But it was his response to the music of his own time that branded him as a true 'young Fogey'. The following letter sounds more like the hand-wringing of an old campaigner than the fire in the belly of a twenty-six-year-old Messiah:

*October 1859: Spohr is dead! He was probably the last of those who still belonged to an artistic period more satisfying than the one in which we now suffer. In those days one might well have looked about eagerly after each fair to see what new and beautiful things had arrived from one composer to another. Now things are different. For months and years now I have hardly seen a single collection of music that gave me pleasure, but a great many that almost caused me physical pain. At no time has any art been so mistreated as is our beloved music now. Let us hope that somewhere in obscurity something better may emerge, for otherwise our epoch will go down in the annals of art as a pit of trash.*

And if his worst fears were to be realized, he was in no doubt as to the likely culprits. Their headquarters were in Weimar, of which he retained mainly disagreeable memories from his first and only visit in 1853 (see p. 25), their patron saints were Liszt and Wagner, they styled themselves the 'Neo-Germans' and their mission was to forge 'the music of the future'. As well as its programmatic and referential doctrines, this music posed a serious threat to the stable key structures which had underpinned all Western art music for centuries (witness, among other things, Liszt's late *Bagatelle Without Tonality* and the chromatic menaces of Wagner's *Tristan*, which, as it turned out, did indeed lead to the music of the future – and, be it said, to an unprecedented gap between composer and listener which yawned ever wider until the conservative backlash of the late twentieth century).

In the Germany of the mid-nineteenth century, music had become deeply politicized. At one extreme lay the pioneering subversives of Weimar and beyond, at the other, the intransigent conservatives of Leipzig (the city of Bach and Mendelssohn, which was just as hidebound in Bach's day as in Brahms's). Of these, the avant-garde, as ever, was the more stridently vocal. Its principal literary organ was the *Neue Zeitschrift für Musik*, founded by Schumann in 1834 (see p. 79) as the opening salvo in his self-styled 'battle of the Band of David against the Philistines'. In 1844, the journal had passed into the hands of Franz Brendel, under whose guidance it became, in effect, the official mouthpiece of the Neo-German movement. Brahms occupied a middle-ground between these two extremes, which gave him the privilege of being attacked by both camps at once. While the Neo-Germans regarded him as a relatively innocuous conservative, the upright Leipzigers saw him as an intolerable modernist. Their reception in 1859 of his great D minor Piano Concerto has become a classic of pig-headedness, and despite his extraordinarily philosophical response (see p. 83), it dealt him a crushing blow. As he put it to Joachim at the time:

*My concerto here was a glittering and decisive – fiasco. The first rehearsal evoked no feelings in performers or listeners. At the second there was no listener, and not a muscle moved in the musicians' faces. And after the performance proper three hands started slowly to clap at the end, but a noisy hissing from all sides forbade any such demonstration. There is nothing more to say about this episode, for not a single soul has said a word to me about the work.*

That was still to come. Thus the critic Edward Bernsdorf, for the conservatives:

*This concerto is composition dragged to its grave. This work cannot give pleasure; it has nothing to offer but hopeless desolation and aridity. For more than three quarters of an hour one must endure this rooting and rummaging, this straining and tugging, this tearing and patching of phrases and flourishes! Not only must one take in this fermenting mass; one must also swallow a dessert of the shrillest dissonances and most unpleasant sounds. Herr Brahms has deliberately made the piano part as uninteresting as possible. It contains no effective treatment of the instrument, no new and ingenious passages, and wherever something appears which gives promise of effect, it is immediately crushed and suffocated by a thick crust of orchestral accompaniment.*

And for the Neo-Germans, a more favourable account from a committed Lisztian, Ferdinand Gleich:

*The work suggests a condition of indefiniteness and fermentation, a wrestling for a method of expression commensurate with the ideals of the composer, which has indeed broken through the form of tradition, but not yet constructed another sufficiently definite and rounded to satisfy the aesthetic demands of art. The first movement, especially, gives us the impression of monstrosity.*

It's hard, today, for those of us who love Brahms's music to comprehend the vitriolic antipathy he aroused in many people. And not only in Germany, but in England (where he was repeatedly savaged by George Bernard Shaw, then a music critic), the United States, Russia (where Tchaikovsky hailed him as a 'giftless bastard' and a 'self-inflated mediocrity') and throughout continental Europe. A year after the failure of his concerto in Leipzig, his Serenade in A for small orchestra elicited the following bouquet in Hanover: 'Brahms's Serenade is a monstrosity, a caricature, a freak which should never have been published, much less performed. It is inexcusable that such filth should have been offered to a public thirsting for good music.' 'Monstrosity' seems to have been the critical buzzword of the day, at least where Brahms was concerned.

In 1860, the year following the débâcle of the D minor Concerto, Brahms was roused to fury by an editorial in the *Neue Zeitschrift* which flatly declared that 'even the north Germans' (of whom Brahms was far and away the most distinguished) had been won over and that 'all the most prominent musicians of the day' now supported the 'Music of the Future'. Spurred by this unwarranted assertion, Brahms, still only twenty-seven, persuaded Joachim to join him in drafting for publication a manifesto attacking the pernicious influence of the Neo-Germans, and the *Neue Zeitschrift* for promoting it.

*The above journal continually spreads the view that musicians of more serious endeavour are fundamentally in agreement with the tendencies it represents, that they recognize in the compositions by the leaders of this group works of artistic value and that altogether, and especially in north Germany, the contentions for and against the so-called 'music of the future' are concluded, and the dispute settled in its favour ... The undersigned ... declare that ... the principles stated by Brendel's journal are not recognized, and that they regard the productions of the leaders and pupils of the so-called 'New German' school ... as contrary to the innermost spirit of music, strongly to be deplored and condemned.*

Once this ill-advised text had been finalized, Joachim set out to canvass the support, and to harvest the signatures, of noted musicians throughout Germany. Many refused point-blank, some agreed, but in the event, and for reasons never satisfactorily explained, the manifesto was printed prematurely, with only four signatures, of which two belonged to relative nonentities. Its only effect, with few exceptions, was to make Brahms the laughing-stock of musical Germany. Thereafter he took care to hold his tongue, at least in public, and addressed himself as a composer to the serious business of proving his point.

In his search for other like-minded composers, Brahms, especially in his later days, was constantly on the lookout for young talent which might help stem the tide of Neo-German 'futurism'. As honorary president of the Wiener Tonkünstler-verein, he was a zealous promoter of competitions to bring promising young talents to the fore. Of the several composers whom he assisted, often anonymously, none

*Karl Tausig, Brahms's friend and Liszt's favourite pupil. As pianist and arranger he looked set to inherit Liszt's mantle before death took him at 29.*

brought him greater pleasure than Dvořák, who owed his international career to Brahms above all others. The full extent of Brahms's support may be gauged by a letter in which the incredulous Dvořák writes, 'I am deeply glad that Brahms is so interested in my music, but I find it hard to understand why he even took on the very tedious job of proof-reading [my manuscripts]. I don't believe there is another musician of his stature in the entire world who would do such a thing.'

After 1860, Brahms himself took no part in the factionalism which purportedly divided the musical world into warring camps of Brahmsians and Wagnerites. Nor did he rise to the bait of Wagner's own contemptuous, malicious and egregiously personal attacks on both him and his music. For some of Wagner's works, indeed, Brahms felt a genuine enthusiasm, and he had a healthy respect even for that far greater body which he found boring, repellent or both. In his later, Viennese years he was a regular visitor to the opera on Wagner nights and could round with unexpected ferocity on those who disparaged the music. When a junior colleague opined in his presence that 'Wagner must be held chiefly responsible for the confusion prevailing in the heads of us young people', Brahms roared, 'Nonsense! The *misunderstood* Wagner has done that. Those understand *nothing* of the real Wagner who are led astray by him. Wagner's is one of the clearest heads that ever existed in the world.' Brahms's claims that he himself understood Wagner's music better than anyone were exaggerated, but were aimed in part at distancing himself from his own supporters. In 1887, he wrote to Joachim from Vienna:

*Wagner is here and I shall probably be called a Wagnerite, mainly of course out of the opposition to which any sensible person is driven by the haughty way in which the musicians here rail against him. Besides, I particularly like to be with Cornelius and Tausig, who claim not to be, nor ever to have been, followers of Liszt, and who can achieve more with their little finger than other musicians with the whole head and all their fingers.\**

*

In 1869, Brahms made his permanent home in Vienna, where he had become an increasingly familiar figure. Given his long-standing reverence for the masters of the past, the only wonder is that he hadn't done it sooner. From the time of his first visit in 1862 he had been entranced by its living sense of history. In March of the following year, he wrote to a friend:

*I have spent a whole winter here, very much at a loose end, but rather enjoyably and cheerfully. I regret above all things that I didn't know Vienna before. The gaiety of the town, the beauty of the surroundings, the sympathetic and vivacious public, how stimulating all these are to the artist! In addition we have in particular the sacred memory of great musicians whose lives and works are brought daily to our minds. In the case of Schubert especially, one has the impression of his being still alive. Again and again one meets people who talk of him as a good friend; again and again one comes across new works, the existence of which was unknown and which are so untouched that one can scrape the very writing-sand off them.*

Among these treasures was a group of Schubert waltzes which entranced him and led in due course to his own set of sixteen Waltzes, op. 39 and the two books of delectable *Liebeslieder* Waltzes, of which the most liltingly Schubertian may be heard on CD1. But with each new discovery, his elation was tempered by a deepening concern:

*Enjoyable and gratifying as their perusal undoubtedly is, everything else is quite melancholy. I have a great many manuscripts here, of which there exists not even a*

---

*Karl Tausig, a good friend of Brahms, was one of the greatest pianists of all time but died tragically of typhoid at the age of twenty-nine.

*Brahms in his
apartment in Vienna,
not long before his
clean-shaven cheeks
yielded to the famous
beard. Coloured
drawing by Fritz
Wichgraf.*

*single copy! The other day a whole pile of unpublished compositions were offered
here at a ridiculously low price. Fortunately the Society of the Friends of Music
acquired them. But how many gems of this type are scattered here and there in private
hands, which either guard them like fiends or else unconcernedly let them disappear!*

Brahms's interest in the music of the past was not a hobby; it was almost an
obsession. He burned with a passionate indignation at the way in which many of
the greatest masters had been either forgotten or consciously swept aside as irrelev-
ant to the needs and tastes of the present. This, however, was nothing new. Schubert's own knowledge of the past went little further back than Bach, if at all: of the
earlier baroque and Renaissance composers he was entirely ignorant. Mozart had
only discovered the music of Bach and Handel at the age of thirty-two, three years
before his death. And though one of the hallmarks of the romantic movement was
a new reverence for the past, that reverence was more literary than musical, and
more generalized than specific. When Brahms came of age, most of Bach's works
were still unknown and unpublished (a generation after Mendelssohn had ostensibly kick-started a Bach revival with his mounting of the *St Matthew Passion* in
1829), Haydn was known only by a small minority of pieces, and Schubert continued
to be undiscovered and unexplored for generations still to come (astonishingly, in

1928, the centenary of his death, no less a figure than Rachmaninov was unaware
of the very existence of Schubert's piano sonatas). Brahms could fairly be said to
have belonged to the first generation of great musicologists, and many of these were
his friends and close associates. He was also the first great composer to bring a
scholar's methodology and thoroughness to the study of earlier music, and the first
regularly to mount performances of it for the general public. His scores were meticulously marked by him in accordance with the fruits of his researches (undertaken
at all the major libraries of Austria and Germany) and show a then unprecedented
concern for the composer's original intentions. As a prolific and painstaking editor,
he prepared performing editions of a repertoire whose breadth is impressive even
by today's musicologically saturated standards. His most important editions were
those of Couperin, Handel, C. P. E. Bach, Chopin and Schumann, but there were
many others as well. Amongst the carefully annotated scores in his library at
the time of his death were examples by Arbeau, Banchieri, Bononcini, Buxtehude,
Byrd, Caldara, Campra, Carissimi, Cavalli, Clemens non Papa, Corelli, Dowland,
Frescobaldi, Froberger, Gabrieli, Hassler, Lassus, Lully, Marenzio, Pachelbel,
Rameau, Scheidt, Vivaldi, Willaert and Zarlino. No less exhaustive were his attentions to the realm of German folk music, a repertoire which he loved as much as
any and which occupied his mind for almost half a century.

Brahms's historical proclivities were not, however, confined to music. He also
took a lively interest in politics, greatly admired the historical works of Sybel and
Treitschke, and had a passionate admiration for Bismarck, on whom, according to
Hanslick, he had read virtually everything in print, and of whom he had a collection
of portraits. Less surprising was his love of painting and architecture. On their visit
together to Italy in 1888, his friend Widmann observed for the first time Brahms's
profound kinship with the masters of the Italian Renaissance. 'Their buildings, their
statues, their pictures were his delight and when one witnessed the absorbed
devotion with which he contemplated their works, or heard him admire in the old
masters a trait conspicuous in himself, their conscientious perfection of detail, even
where it could hardly be noticeable to the ordinary observer, one could not help
instituting the comparison between himself and them.'

By that time, Brahms had long since transcended the assaults of those critics
who had bedevilled him in earlier days. Liszt and Wagner were dead, and he was
now generally regarded, all over the world, as the greatest of living composers. Not
that he was without his detractors. He was always, and remains, a controversial
composer. It would be foolish to pretend that he was not gratified by the popularity
he now enjoyed. What had he said to Billroth at the time of the First Symphony?
'You cannot imagine how beautiful and heart-warming it is to sense a sympathy
like yours. In such a moment one realizes that this is the best part of composing

Eduard Hanslick
censer-swinging at
the feet of the
bepedestalled Brahms
(from Figaro, Vienna
1890).

Eduard Hanslick censer-swinging at the feet of the bepedestalled Brahms (from Figaro, Vienna 1890).

and all that is connected with it.' Of course he was gratified. But at no time did it turn his head. When asked, three years before his death, to speculate on his likely treatment by posterity he remarked, 'I know very well the place I shall one day have in the history of music: the place that Cherubini once had and has today. That is my lot – my fate.' As a prophet, he turns out to have been wide of the mark.

\*

As he entered his sixties, Brahms looked old beyond his years, an impression due in part to his flowing white beard. It was only in the last few months of his life, however, that his robust good health and bounding energy deserted him. By that time he was mortally ill, but it was still to be some time before he realized it. Late in the summer of 1896 he wrote to Kalbeck, 'One very hot day, when I set out to walk from Ischl to Lauffen, I was so deep in thought that I just walked and walked, without looking about me much; and so, to my astonishment, I was all of a sudden in Steg [some eight miles distant]. Then, in addition, I walked back a good stretch of the way. That night I was so ill I thought I was going to die, and went from one swoon into another. It seems that I had already been suffering from jaundice for six weeks.' Some days later he was visited by his friend Otto Bauer, who was struck by his curious behaviour. 'He gave me a glass to hold, poured cognac into it, and intentionally made it overflow. Then he seized my dripping hand and licked it off. I was stupefied with surprise and asked him why he did that. "Oh," came the answer, "the doctors now forbid me to drink; but they say not a word about licking!" '

It soon became clear that Brahms was afflicted by something more serious than jaundice. He was suffering from an incurable cancer of the liver, the same disease that had killed his father a quarter-century earlier. Doctors and friends attempted to conceal it from him, and he himself made light of his malady in letters to his friends, but his condition worsened so quickly and so visibly that no one could doubt the truth. His final decline is best described by those who witnessed it.

Professor Julius Wachsmann dined with him two months before his death:

*The portly old gentleman evidently straining his weak eyesight in the library of his friend Viktor von Miller zu Aichholz.*

*Our hostess had curtained the windows heavily and put red bulbs in the electric light sockets, so that the Master's dark greenish bronze complexion would not be conspicuous. One noticed his terrifying colour only in the daylight of the ante-room. He ate and drank a lot. With his coffee he demanded a large amount of rum. Tenderly admonished by the daughter of the house that it would not be good for him, he insisted, exclaiming 'Ach, that will make no difference' – words which showed his realization that he was doomed.*

Richard Specht confirms the extent of Brahms's physical deterioration:

*Never have I seen such a devastation in a man within so short a period. His mighty, sturdy figure shrank to that of a very old man, his face was a yellowish brown, his skin like leather, his wonderful blue eyes dull, with the whites gone yellow as quinces, his hair dry and brittle, his hands cold and hard. He gave me a heart-rending glance and I could just contrive to keep my countenance. The changes his illness had wrought in him manifested themselves psychically as well as physically. He had grown quite tender and communicative; 'I have even given up being rude to people,' he once said in a kind of sad astonishment. But what one could not help noticing was the effort every step cost him, the dreadful lassitude with which the man dragged himself along who not long before was difficult to keep pace with on a walk in the country.*

In his final weeks, even reading tired him. He complained that he could no longer retain what he read, and that the only subject that now interested him was Bismarck. He would sit at his window, gazing out, silent and alone with his thoughts.

On 7 March 1897, he was conveyed to the directors' box at the Gesellschaft der Musikfreunde to hear his Fourth Symphony conducted by Hans Richter. Specht was also there:

*The public was in a frenzy of enthusiasm. But when Richter pointed to the box where only now Brahms was discovered, deathly pale, a hurricane broke out. There were deafening calls, cries and clapping, people stood on their seats the better to see the Master's terribly ravaged figure, hats and handkerchiefs waved to him, he was obliged to come to the edge of the box repeatedly. The acclamations simply would not end. The audience knew they were seeing Brahms for the last time, and he knew it as well. He stood there, both hands convulsively grasping the plush covering of the balustrade, silent sobs shaking his wasted body; once more he inclined his head, with its long hair now thin and wiry, and then stepped back. Vienna and Brahms had taken leave of each other.*

Four weeks later Dr Josef Breuer, the doctor who attended Brahms in his last illness (and, incidentally, a collaborator with Freud in the founding of psycho-analysis) went to his son, also a doctor, and told him, 'Brahms is nearly finished. Would you go and spend the night watching over him?'

*Of course I was glad to. When I arrived at Karlsgasse 4, and was presented to the Master, he was very weak, but still kind and thoughtful, and showed hospitable concern about finding the best place for me to rest. He slept until half-past one, then grew uneasy. I asked whether he had pain. 'Yes,' he said, 'but it is not unbearable.' Then he slept. Again, about four, I heard him tossing, and offered to give him an injection. He said, 'Perhaps it would be better.' When this was done, I asked him if he would like some wine, and he nodded. So I poured him out a glassful of the fine old Rhine wine from his friend the Duke of Meiningen's cellars, which had been put out for me by the housekeeper. With scarcely any assistance, Brahms sat up, drank it off in two draughts, and, in his hoarse north-German voice, exclaimed with satisfaction: 'Ja, das ist schön!' [Yes, that is beautiful!]. Then he slept, and was still asleep at seven, when I was forced to hasten to my clinic.*

At half-past eight that morning, 3 April 1897, Brahms's housekeeper, Frau Truxa, came into his room. 'When I went to his bedside, he sat up, and tried to tell me something. But his plate of artificial teeth kept falling down and prevented him from speaking. When he found that these attempts were useless, great tears came into his eyes and rolled down his wasted cheeks. Gazing wistfully at me, he sank back and drew his last breath.'

Brahms himself would never have countenanced the funeral accorded him. The procession as it made its way through the streets of Vienna stretched further than the eye could see, the windows all along the route were crammed with spectators, some weeping, others merely curious; dignitaries from many countries had travelled to Vienna and joined the throng; in Hamburg, the flags of every nation represented in the harbour were flown at half-mast, flowers and messages flowed in, wreaths were sent and laid by royalty and countless ordinary people who had perhaps never even seen Brahms but who had felt their lives immeasurably enriched by his music. On the brilliantly sunny afternoon of 6 April 1897, Brahms was laid to rest near the graves of Beethoven and Schubert. Cherubini would have approved.

# CD Commentary

**CD1**   **Scherzo in C minor for Violin and Piano ('F–A–E')**

With the exception of the magnificent F minor Sonata for piano, this is the earliest of Brahms's works to have found a permanent place in the mainstream repertoire. Written in 1853, when he was twenty, it originally formed part of a composite sonata, composed as a greeting to Joachim from Schumann, Brahms and their mutual friend Albert Dietrich. Dietrich contributed the first movement, Schumann the Intermezzo and Finale, and Brahms the Scherzo. The only movement to have found favour with posterity, it derives its nickname from Joachim's motto *'Frei aber einsam'* (Free but lonely). The authorship of the sonata was kept a secret until Joachim had played it through, but he identified the respective composers with no trouble. The sonata remained in Joachim's possession and it was only in 1906 that he sanctioned the publication of Brahms's Scherzo, nine years after the composer's death. The other movements have survived and are justly neglected.

## Piano Concerto no. 1 in D minor, op. 15

Like the First Symphony, though not so extremely, the D minor Piano Concerto was a long time brewing – a fact which the seamless unity of the finished product manages artfully to conceal. Nor would one guess from the epic seriousness and

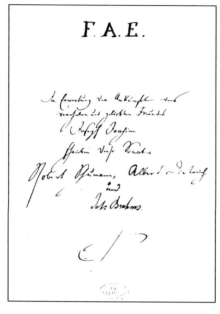

*The original manuscript title page of the 'F–A–E' Sonata for Violin and Piano, written jointly by Schumann, Brahms and Dietrich in honour of their friend Joachim. Brahms's contribution was the Scherzo (CD1).*

grandeur of the work (the most strenuously sober of all great tone poems) that it is the work of a very young man. It was begun in 1854, when Brahms was still very much the beautiful, beardless youth pictured on page 62. The stout, hirsute curmudgeon whose eyes, with their record of hurt and sorrow, stare out at us from so many portraits, was still a long way off. The sorrow and hurt, however, were already there. Like so many other works of Brahms, the piece is intimately bound up with the Schumanns. It was, after all, within a year of their first meeting that Robert lost his reason and cast himself into the Rhine. So much has been made of Clara's grief and of Brahms's lovesick attentions to her in her hour of greatest need that one easily forgets the enormity of the tragedy for Brahms himself.

The first musical fruit of his own acute distress was a sonata in D minor for two pianos, though Schumann, as we've seen, had predicted with his famous reference to 'veiled symphonies' that the piano would soon seem to Brahms too limited a medium for the immensity of his musical conceptions. Ironically and appropriately it was in the making of this very work that Schumann's prophecy came true. Only a few weeks after beginning the piece, Brahms voiced his growing frustration to Joachim, complaining that even two pianos were inadequate to the work's requirements. Shortly thereafter, the sonata was abandoned, but its first movement soon resurfaced, considerably amended, as the beginning of a D minor symphony (not coincidentally, the key of Beethoven's Ninth). Unsurprisingly, in view of the fact that this marked Brahms's first foray into the realm of orchestration, this version too proved unsatisfactory, and within a year or so of its inception the work acquired a third lease of life as a concerto.

Though the work is immensely difficult to play, it wholly abjures the bravura display which was the fashion at the time of its inception. In terms of both material and texture, piano and orchestra meet, for the most part, not as gladiatorial adversaries but as equal if contrasting partners in a drama of authentically symphonic proportions. Though its three movements were conceived at different times and were subjected to many revisions, the work is remarkable alike for its spiritual integrity and its thematic unity. The robust main theme of the Finale, for instance, is based directly on the warmly autumnal eloquence of the first movement's second subject, just as the first theme of the Adagio derives from the opening theme of the work as a whole. And the themes of the first movement itself bear a similar kinship. The slow movement is an early example of Brahms's ability to cast music of the most heart-clutching sadness in the major mode.

## *Liebeslieder* Waltzes, op. 52

No music reflects Brahms's immersion in Viennese life better than his *Liebeslieder Walzer* (literally, Love-song Waltzes) for four voices and piano duet. After the first publication, Brahms wrote to Clara, 'I must confess that it was the first time I smiled at the sight of a printed work of mine! I will risk being called an ass if our *Liebeslieder* don't give pleasure to a few people.' It was no risk at all. The first book, composed in 1868–9, proved so popular that Brahms followed it up with a second collection in 1874. He later made two arrangements, one for piano alone, the other (of only nine songs) for voices and orchestra. With only one exception, all the songs are settings of Russian and Polish folk poetry, and none is more typical of Brahms's Viennese mood than the one recorded here.

## *Schicksalslied*, op. 54

Published in 1871, three years after the German Requiem, the *Schicksalslied* (Song of Destiny) was spontaneously inspired by the poem by Hölderlin from which it draws its text. The story goes that Brahms was so moved by the poem on discovering it in a friend's library that he began setting it to music on the spot. The contrast between the serene calm of the gods on Mount Olympus and the restless, unhappy destiny of the mortals was a natural for Brahms, most of whose major choral works are concerned in one way or another with death and human destiny. And for all his objections to programmatic writing it's hard not to feel the continuous beating of the drums throughout the introduction as representative of destiny itself. Among the many beauties of this very beautiful work is the anticipation of the choral entry at the end of the introduction. The scoring is full of deft touches, not least in the use of the woodwind, and the combination of strings, brass and chorus at the start of the agitated central Allegro strikes just the right note of unrest, without going over the top, Liszt fashion. The return of the serene material of the opening in the work's final section (albeit in a different key), is convincing musically but departs utterly from the stark juxtapositions of the poem itself, which brings no such consolatory message of hope at the end. Some commentators, rejecting the possibility that Brahms is uncharacteristically donning rose-tinted spectacles here, have interpreted this final section as emphasizing the complete indifference of the gods to the travails of humanity.

## CD2              Symphony no. 2 in D major, op. 73

Like the great Violin Concerto of the following year (1878), it was written during the summer while Brahms was staying at the lakeside Austrian town of Pörtschach. And while it isn't without its shadows, it breathes an air of serenity, contentment and good humour seldom encountered in the more dramatic and intense works of his earliest manhood. Yet even here, in what is perhaps the most purely Brahmsian work he'd written to date, the public would not let him escape comparison with Beethoven. Just as Bülow had labelled the First Symphony 'Beethoven's Tenth', so now people called the new symphony Brahms's 'Pastoral', and it isn't hard to see why for there are frequent echoes of the *spirit* of that enchanting work. Brahms also uses a structural device famously employed by Beethoven in his celebrated Fifth, namely deriving most of his thematic material from the first three notes of the opening movement. In both the outer movements, Brahms builds his principal themes round the simple three-note chord which serves as the anchor for the home key of the work as a whole, and as the unifying goal behind most of his subsequent themes.

## Piano Trio no. 3 in C minor, op. 101

Brahms's habit of requesting the severest criticism of his works by such close and esteemed friends as Joachim and Clara Schumann would seem to have had a double motive. On the one hand, he was genuinely interested in their comments and suggestions, even if he seldom put them into practice; on the other, and in keeping with the rest of humanity, he craved approval. In the case of the C minor Trio, he obviously struck gold as far as Clara was concerned. As she wrote in her diary in June 1887:

*I experienced my greatest pleasure on the 20th, as at last I felt strong enough to try the wonderfully touching Trio in C minor. What a composition it is! Ingenious throughout in its passion, its strength of thought, its charm, its expression. No other of Johannes's works has ever so completely overwhelmed me . . . I am happier tonight than I have been for a long time.*

Charm, for most listeners, is not one of its more obvious characteristics. Despite the relative calm of the Andante, described by Donald Francis Tovey as 'a child of the gods, free from terror', the work belies the outward calm that characterized Brahms's demeanour during the evidently happy summers he spent in Switzerland in the 1880s. It is at once the most concise, the most passionate and the stormiest of his trios, recalling the *Sturm und Drang* ('storm and stress') of his early works. Again the key is significant. C minor denotes Brahms at his most concentrated and serious, even tragic,* and the opening movement here is true to type (unusually, Brahms retains the tonality of C for all four movements, though the third is cast in major). In the second movement, a scherzo in all but name (and again in C minor), both stringed instruments play with mutes throughout, creating a unique and haunting sonority typical of Brahms's often underestimated colouristic imagination. The third movement, tellingly headed 'Andante grazioso' and sticking to the tonality of C, though here in the major, was originally cast in the exotic time signature of 7/4 – and Brahms's second thought was only slightly less unusual: repeated groupings of one bar in 4/4 plus two in 2/4. According to one friend we have here an exceptionally candid study in self-portraiture: 'Better than any photograph, it is the most truthful picture of the master.'

## German Folk-songs

In 1860, Brahms wrote to Clara, 'Song-writing is now sailing such a wrong tack that one can never do enough to impress upon one's self the ideal, which for me is the folk-song.' The fact that many of the songs he actually set turned out not to be authentic is neither here nor there. They all embody the characteristics of German folk-song, and Brahms lavished no less love and care on these settings than on his most genuinely original songs. And indeed they all have the feel of original Brahms. He had absorbed and been nourished by these songs all his life but it was only near the end of his career that he fulfilled a long-cherished dream and enshrined them in the single largest collection of songs he ever produced, the forty-nine *Deutsche Volkslieder* which he published in 1894. His pride in this collection ranked with the

*The First Symphony is perhaps the greatest example. Others include the Third Piano Quartet, the First String Quartet and the F–A–E Scherzo.

greatest pleasures of his final years. As he confessed to Clara, 'This is perhaps the first time that I look forward with real pleasure to correcting the proofs, and to the publication of a work of mine.' Obviously he had forgotten saying exactly the same thing about the *Liebeslieder*. The collection was intended primarily for domestic use, and Brahms objected strenuously to its appropriation by stars of the concert stage. It's hard to imagine, however, that he could find anything but delight in the performances recorded here, artful though they are.

## CD3                    Violin Sonata no. 3 in D minor, op. 108

The last of Brahms's three violin sonatas, composed between 1886 and 1888, is also far and away the most dramatic. The key alone gives a clue to its character. Like his revered Mozart, Brahms seems from the First Piano Concerto onwards to have associated D minor with tragedy, but as with Beethoven, his tragedy is frequently accompanied by an element of defiance and a driving rhythmic momentum. There is perhaps no other violin sonata that conveys such a sense of excitement. Among its several unusual characteristics is the extensive use of so-called pedal-points in the first movement: the entire development section is played out over a continually repeated A (the dominant), a device which recurs in the coda, this time on the tonic D. As in the D minor Concerto, the profoundly affecting slow movement is an interesting and relatively rare example of melancholy expressed in the major mode. The Scherzo is cast in the distant key of F sharp minor, and bears a distinct spiritual kinship with the equivalent movement of the C minor Trio (see pp. 152–3). The Finale is a Presto agitato in Brahms's most thrillingly virtuosic manner. Though one would hardly guess it, much of the sonata (like its spiritual sister, the C minor Trio) was conceived and written during the idyllic summer months Brahms spent by the shores of Lake Thun in Switzerland.

## Clarinet Quintet in B minor, op. 115

One of the most intensely lyrical and gently melancholic of all Brahms's chamber works, the Clarinet Quintet of 1891 is the richest and most searching of the four late works inspired by the playing of Richard Mühlfeld (the others being the two Sonatas for clarinet and piano and the Trio for clarinet, piano and cello). The clarinet had been regarded even in the classical era as the most 'romantic' of the wind instruments, and Brahms here draws liberally on its mellow and strangely 'nostalgic' properties, as his beloved Mozart had done before him. The last movement demonstrates the variation technique of which Brahms had been a master since his youth, and ends with a poignant look back to the very opening of the work.

## Four Piano Pieces, op. 119

Although they are the last group of Brahms's piano pieces, completed in 1893, when the composer was sixty, some of the pieces comprising op. 119 may well have been composed earlier. And while there is no reason why they shouldn't be performed separately, it seems clear that Brahms envisaged them as a steadily accelerating

*Brahms photographed by his friend Maria Fellinger in 1894. Within the next few years, cancer would drastically change his appearance.*

group, advancing from what may be the slowest movement he ever wrote to the triumphant and magnificent E flat Rhapsody.

Not even the much-scorned Liszt could have devised a more surprising or wistfully enchanting thematic transformation than that achieved by Brahms in the second Intermezzo – a monothematic Andantino, whose lilting, waltz-like middle section in E major is derived straight from the fragmentary, anxious questionings of the opening E minor section.

The third piece, the swan-song of Brahms's intermezzi, is the most light-hearted of them all, and has enjoyed a venerable career outside the set as a popular encore with piano recitalists. Here the shadows cast in the first two pieces are dispersed, and the tempo is the quickest yet. Set in the sunny key of C major, this is pianistically among the least taxing of Brahms's quicker movements, but its characteristic rhythmic ambiguities pose stimulating challenges even to the subtlest interpreters.

The big-boned, extroverted E flat Rhapsody which closes the set brings Brahms's output for solo piano to a triumphantly positive close, though there is perhaps an element of Beethovenian fist-shaking in the defiant coda, which ends, unexpectedly, in the minor. Its almost tub-thumping opening theme (if one chooses to hear it that way) was for a long time saddled by musical wags with the words 'I have been/ saved by the/Salvation/Army, damn! damn! damn!', and it too teases the interpreter with unusual rhythmic possibilities.

# Further Reading

## Correspondence

The most absorbing biographical material is always and inevitably the living correspondence of the personalities involved. Fully sixteen volumes were published
between 1906 and 1922 by the Deutsches Brahms-Gesellschaft in Berlin, but only
the first two of these, *Johannes Brahms: The Herzogenberg Correspondence*, edited
by Max Kalbeck (London, 1909), have ever been available in English. Until very
recently, non-German-speakers have been curiously ill-served where Brahms's letters are concerned, but this lamentable state of affairs has now been royally righted
with the publication by Oxford University Press of the 800-page *Johannes Brahms:
Life and Letters*, translated by Josef Eisinger and edited by Styra Avins (1997). This
is likely to remain the definitive English version, and can hardly be recommended
too highly. Nevertheless, alternative translations are always fascinating and frequently of value, and dedicated letter-hounds would do well to seek out a number
of useful and illuminating collections which have long been out of print. Of these,
the most engrossing is undoubtedly the correspondence of Brahms and Clara Schumann (or what remains of it), edited by Berthold Litzmann and published in both
English and German in 1927. Much interesting material is also to be found in Nora
Bickley's selection and translation of the Joachim correspondence, published in
London back in 1914. German-speaking Brahmsians should also find much

satisfaction in the volumes which have been issuing from the Hamburg Brahms-Gesellschaft since 1975, under the title *Brahms-Studien*.

## Life and Works

Of the several excellent biographies, Malcolm MacDonald's substantial, thoughtful and wide-ranging study in the Master Musicians series (London, 1990) can be very highly recommended indeed. Engagingly but not ingratiatingly written, it contains a wealth of information from an impressive variety of sources, and while much of the musical commentary is more descriptive than truly analytical (of how many musical books can this *not* be said?), it gives a valuable overview of Brahms's output and helps to deepen our understanding of it in the context of its time, and beyond. Readers without a working knowledge of musical terms, forms and techniques may occasionally find the going rather heavy, but the book is so organized that one can easily skip over the strictly musical discussion and read it as straight biography.

Comparable in scope and substance, though not so musicologically up-to-date, is Karl Geiringer's excellent *Brahms: His Life and Work* (London, 1948), which pretty well led the field until MacDonald's book. The prose (translated from the German) is perhaps a little academic at times, but he writes feelingly of the composer and authoritatively of the music, and the many quotations from letters, journals etc. add a real sense of immediacy to the narrative.

Few of Brahms's biographers can claim to have performed virtually all of his keyboard music, and to have conducted much of his choral and orchestral music into the bargain, but Professor Ivor Keys is just such a man. His excellent and highly readable *Johannes Brahms* (London, 1989) is both enjoyable and illuminating. Biography and musical commentary are neatly segregated, as in the standard life-and-works format, which gives you, in effect, two slightish books for the price of one. Sources and quotations are not as meticulously documented as in MacDonald's book (frustratingly for the scholarly inclined), but the material is skilfully deployed and the story well told.

The late Hans Gal, too, was musician first and writer second, and his enjoyable if rather slight study, *Johannes Brahms: His Work and Personality* (London, 1963), is worth seeking out – probably in a library, since a reprint is unlikely.

Of scholarly symposia, *Brahms and His World*, edited by Walter Frisch (Princeton, 1990), can be highly recommended, especially for the readability and interest of its biographical essays, memoirs etc., whereas Michael Musgrave's *Brahms 2: biographical, documentary and analytical studies* (Cambridge, 1987), while it has undoubted value, is really a book aimed at scholars and the musicologically inclined, and the general reader is likely to feel sidelined.

## Biography and Reminiscence

No biography gives us a more immediate and engaging portrait than Florence May's *The Life of Johannes Brahms* (London, 1905). Brahms's first English biographer, she knew and had studied with Brahms, as readers of this book will already know, and though she has been accused of lacking sufficient detachment, she includes plenty of material on the more negative aspects of Brahms's personality. If he emerges finally as profoundly lovable in spite of himself, the author is not entirely to blame: it was the experience of countless people who knew him. Case-hardened bibliophiles may find the lack of scholarly documentation a little frustrating, but the book is a mine of information, quotation and reminiscence, delightfully and stylishly presented, and the author was an indefatigable researcher, not for a moment relying on her own experiences and memories, but seeking out and grilling a wide variety of witnesses.

Less engaging and more self-consciously written but no less illuminating, in its way, is Robert Haven Schauffler's *The Unknown Brahms* (New York, 1933), also long out of print. The first book to tackle head-on the question of Brahms's sexuality (hence the 'unknown' of the title), it doesn't avoid an element of sensationalism, and its ostensibly sympathetic moralizing has a strong whiff of fashionable hypocrisy about it, but the wealth of anecdote and first-hand evidence make it an invaluable source. The author sought out, interviewed and subsequently quoted, sometimes extensively, many who had known Brahms in one capacity or another.

Of personal reminiscences, three, much quoted in the present book, stand out as especially valuable and absorbing: the *Memoirs of Eugenie Schumann* (London, 1927), Sir George Henschel's *Personal Recollections of Johannes Brahms* (Boston, 1907) and Dame Ethel Smyth's unique and wonderful *Impressions that Remained* (London, 1919). Also valuable, and quite delightfully written, is Sir Charles Stanford's *Brahms* (New York, 1912; London, 1927). Richard Specht (*Johannes Brahms*, London, 1930) also had the benefit of knowing Brahms personally, though not, one senses, quite as well as he would like us to think, and there's a curious feeling of coldness about his book, but its interest is undeniable.

## The Music

Most of the books and essays on Brahms's music are too technical for the lay reader to get much out of, but one in particular is an outstanding exception: Eric Sams's *Brahms's Songs* (BBC Guide, London, 1972) has inexplicably been out of print for many years now, but should be in the library of every true Brahms lover. Far slimmer and less detailed than his invaluable *The Songs of Robert Schumann*, it is nevertheless packed with shafts of insight and provocative observations and leaves one think-ing, as all good books should. It also leaves one panting to explore the songs at first hand, by whatever means. And there are excellent, and highly approachable, observations to be found, too, in the late Denis Matthews's *Brahms's Piano Music* (BBC Guide, London, 1986) – and at the time of writing, that one *is* in print.

The most exhaustive and ambitious, though not, perhaps, the most penetrating, of all musicological guides is Edwin Evans's *Historical, Descriptive and Analytical Account of the Entire Works of Johannes Brahms* (4 vols., London, 1912–35). Out of print for ages, but good fodder for writers of programme notes. Strictly a library job.

# Further Listening

The other three symphonies, of course. Not because they're 'important', but because they're wonderful – and like all great works, they continue to yield new experiences no matter how often one listens to them – the operative word here being 'listen' as opposed to 'hear'. The first requires attention, the other doesn't. Both are valid ways of experiencing music, whatever the purists say. But neither is sufficient *exclusively*. The First Symphony, so long and tortuous in the making, is in some ways the least approachable. Even Clara Schumann found the opening a bit austere and doom-laden at first, but she soon came round to it. The Third is in some ways the most 'romantic', and after the Second, the most immediate in its appeal. The Fourth is the most grandiose and overpowering, but it's also in many ways the richest and fullest, the most all-embracing in its spiritual scope.

One might almost describe the Second Piano Concerto as a fifth symphony. It has the four-movement structure associated with the symphony, but not the concerto, and the same epic reach. Despite its formidable difficulties for the pianist, it gives us Brahms at his most approachable and secure: awe-inspiring, massive, filled with shimmering cascades of the subtlest colours, tuneful, thrilling, almost impermissibly touching in the slow movement and incomparably dancing and graceful in the Finale, it gives us the fully-rounded Brahms at his best and most generous (it's some measure of the psychological and personal gulf between the two composers that Liszt could have found this work 'rather grey').

The Violin Concerto – the first of Brahms's works openly to court comparison with Beethoven – is likewise symphonic in mood and scope (there is some reason to believe that the 'extra' Scherzo of the Second Piano Concerto was originally intended for this one). Of Brahms's four concertos, this is probably the most popular, despite technical difficulties which ultimately render most soloists inadequate to its demands.

For reasons not easy to understand, the Double Concerto (for violin and cello) has always found greater favour with musicians than with the wider musical public, but the work fairly overflows with lyrical beauty and spiritual warmth, despite its occasional asperities.

Of Brahms's many chamber works, three immediately spring to mind: the great F minor Piano Quintet (yet another undercover symphony), unequalled in stature by any other; the Horn Trio (irresistibly lyrical, moving and exciting by turns), and the G minor Piano Quartet (the symphonic character of this one led Arnold Schoenberg to orchestrate it, with fascinating results). But I wouldn't dream of living without the G major Violin Sonata (Brahms at his most lyrically radiant and serene), or the B flat String Sextet (Brahms at his most rapturously romantic). And who could bypass the two cello sonatas?

Of choral works, the German Requiem has pride of place. In the view of many Brahmsians, and others, this is his greatest work, and would have been included here but for its great length. The 'Alto Rhapsody', Brahms's heart-rendingly tragic 'bridal song' (see p. 109), is his next-best-known choral work, but is surpassed, in my view, by the surprisingly neglected, elegiac *Nänie*, whose beauty and poignancy are almost painful.

The solo songs should really be explored wholesale, as it were, so rich are they in subtlety, range and skill, but off the top of my head I'd single out (in no particular order) *Der Schmied, Die Mainacht, Von ewiger Liebe, Vergebliches Ständchen, An die Nachtigall, Immer leiser wird mein Schlummer, Das Mädchen, Das Mädchen spricht, Sapphische Ode, Alte Liebe, Meine Liebe ist grün, O kühler Wald*, the famous *Wiegenlied* ('Brahms's Lullaby'), *Der Tod, das ist die kühle Nacht*, the *Vier ernste Gesänge* ('Four Serious Songs' – his last and perhaps his greatest), and both books (but especially the first) of the *Liebeslieder* Waltzes.

Of the piano works, the great F minor Sonata and the Four Ballades, op. 10 stand out amongst the earliest; the big variation sets on the 'St Antoni' Chorale and themes by Paganini and Handel are indispensable, but the earlyish D major Variations on an Original Theme are of a beauty seldom surpassed and come from the same world as the D minor Piano Concerto. Of the later sets (opp. 76 and 116–118), the finest are to be found in opp. 117 and 118, but there are jewels in all of them, and the two Rhapsodies (op. 79) have more than earned their popularity. It must be said that very little of Brahms's piano music is easy to play, but there are pieces in each of these sets which are within the reach of the moderately accomplished amateur (in particular, op. 76, nos. 2–4, 6 & 7; op. 79: the G minor Rhapsody; op. 116, nos. 4 & 6; op. 117 complete; op. 118, nos. 1 & 2; op. 119, nos. 1 & 2).

| DATE | LIFE AND WORKS | MUSICAL CONTEXT | HISTORICAL BACKGROUND |
|---|---|---|---|
| 1833 | Birth of Johannes Brahms at no. 24 Specksgang (later no. 60 Speckstrasse) in the Gängeviertel district of Hamburg) on 7 May, second child of Johann Jakob Brahms (27) and Johanna Henrike Christiane Nissen (44): baptised 26 May at the Michaeliskirke. He has an elder sister, Elise, born in 1831. | Birth of Borodin; Bellini 32; Berlioz 30; Bruckner 9; Chopin 23; Donizetti 36; Liszt 22; Meyerbeer 42; Rossini 41; Schumann 23; Verdi 20; Wagner 20. Mendelssohn (24) writes 'Italian' Symphony. | Hanoverian constitution granted by King William (also William IV of England). Liberal student uprising suppressed in Frankfurt. Abolition of slavery in British empire. Factory Act (GB). Civil war in Spain (to 1839): absolutists (supporting Don Carlos and backed by Prussia, Austria and Russia) oppose constitutionalists (supporting Queen Isabella and backed by Britain and France). |
| 1834 | | Berlioz: *Harold en Italie*. Schumann founds *Neue Zeitschrift für Musik* and begins *Etudes symphoniques*. | Prussian customs union (Zollverein) established (excludes Austria). Spanish Inquisition (established 1478) officially ends. Balzac: *Le Père Goriot*. |
| 1835 | Birth of brother Friedrich (Fritz), 26 March. | Birth of Saint-Saëns. Death of Bellini (34). Bellini: *I Puritani*. Donizetti: *Lucia di Lammermoor*. Schumann: *Carnaval*. | Death of Emperor Francis I of Austria: the mentally ill Ferdinand I rules with the help of a regency council dominated by the chancellor, Metternich. First German railway (Nürnberg to Fürth). Strauss: *Das Leben Jesu*. Grillparzer: *Der Traum, ein Leben*. |
| 1836 | | Meyerbeer: *Les Huguenots*. Schumann: *Kreisleriana* (written in three days). Fantasy in C, op. 17. Wagner: *Das Liebesverbot*. | First steam locomotives in Austria (Budweid–Linz); first Austrian steamship company (Trieste). Metternich clamps down on liberal/nationalist movement in Hungary: imprisonment (to 1839) of Kossuth and Wesselényi. Chartist Movement begins in Britain (to 1848). |
| 1837 | Family moves to no. 38 Ulricusstrasse. | Birth of Balakirev. Death of Hummel (59). Berlioz: *Grande Messe des Morts*. Chopin: *Etudes*, op. 25. Schumann: *Davidsbündlertänze*. Lortzing: *Zar und Zimmermann*. | Death of William IV; accession of Victoria (GB). Her uncle, Ernst August, becomes king of Hanover; refuses to recognize constitution of 1833 and exiles leading liberal academics. First major German railway (Dresden–Leipzig): extensive railway building begins in both Germany and Austria. Electric telegraph patented by Cooke and Wheatstone (GB). Dickens: *The Pickwick Papers*. Hegel: *Lessons on the Philosophy of History*. |
| 1838 | | Birth of Bizet and Bruch. Berlioz: *Benvenuto Cellini*. Cherubini: Requiem in D minor. Vol. 1 of Kretzschmer/ Zuccalmaglio *Deutsche Volkslieder* published. | People's Charter drawn up; Anti-Corn Law League established (GB). First steamships in regular transatlantic passenger service. First message sent by Morse telegraph (US). |
| 1839 | Begins music lessons with his father, who is a town musician. Attends a private school in the Dammthorwall. | Birth of Mussorgsky. Berlioz: *Roméo et Juliette*. Verdi: *Oberto, Conte di San Bonifacio*. First performance of Schubert's 'Great' C major Symphony, cond. Mendelssohn. | Prussia and Austria introduce first factory legislation, imposing not very stringent limits on child labour. Belgian independence recognized. Opium War between Britain and China (to 1842). First bicycle constructed. Daguerre and Nièpce announce Daguerrotype process. Baedeker publishes first European travel guides. |

| DATE | LIFE AND WORKS | MUSICAL CONTEXT | HISTORICAL BACKGROUND |
|---|---|---|---|
| 1840 | Continues studies with his father with a view to a career as an orchestral player. | Birth of Tchaikovsky. Death of Paganini (58). Schumann marries Clara Wieck. | Death of Frederick William III of Prussia; accession of Frederick William IV. His initial policies are liberal but he drifts towards a authoritarian bureaucratic regime. Marriage of Queen Victoria and Prince Albert of Saxe-Coburg. Acceleration of industrial development in Prussia and Austria throughout 1840s. |
| 1841 | Begins lessons with Otto Cossel. | Birth of Dvořák, Chabrier, Tausig. Schumann: Symphony no. 1. Saxophone invented. | British sovereignty over Hong Kong proclaimed; New Zealand becomes British colony. August Borsig's Berlin workshop produces first German railway engine. Friedrich List's *National System of Political Economy*. |
| 1842 | Family moves to no. 29 Dammthorwall. Fire destroys much of old Hamburg. | Birth of Massenet and Sullivan. Death of Cherubini (82). Glinka: *Ruslan and Ludmilla*. Rossini: Stabat Mater. Verdi: *Nabucco*. Wagner: *Rienzi* | Peel's tariff reforms (financed by new income tax): Britain moves towards free trade. First use of ether for surgical anaesthesia (USA). First submarine telegraph cable (New York). Gogol: *Dead Souls*. |
| 1843 | First appearance as pianist leads to offer of American tour. Begins studies with Eduard Marxsen. | Birth of Grieg. Balfe: *The Bohemian Girl* Donizetti: *Don Pasquale*. Mendelssohn: *A Midsummer Night's Dream*. Wagner: *Der fliegende Höllander*. | Clashes between Magyars and Croats in Hungarian Diet. Greece adopts a constitution. British expansion in India (Sind) and South Africa (Natal). Faraday establishes general theory of electrolysis. |
| 1844 | Attends secondary school. Composes a sonata which he plays to Louise Japha. | Birth of Rimsky-Korsakov. Verdi: *Ernani*. | Silesian weavers' strike. Dumas: *Les Trois Mousquetaires* and *Le Comte de Monte Cristo*; Heine: *Deutschland: ein Wintermärschen*. |
| 1845 | Marxsen becomes Brahms's sole music teacher. | Birth of Fauré and Widor. Mendelssohn: Violin Concerto in E minor. Schumann: Piano Concerto in A minor completed. Wagner: *Tannhäuser*. | Harvest failure and famine in Germany, particularly in East Prussia and Silesia; customs union obliged to import grain; staple food prices rise by 50%, causing distress to the poorer classes. Swiss Sonderbund formed. Anglo-Sikh war (to 1849). Power loom invented (USA). |
| 1846 | Theory and composition studies; plays the piano in dockside *Animierlokale*. | Berlioz: *La Damnation de Faust*. Mendelssohn: *Elijah*. Schumann: Symphony no. 2. | Berlin–Hamburg railway. German economic crisis. Polish insurrection in Galicia: free city of Cracow incorporated into Austria. Charles VIII moves to consolidate Danish sovereignty over Schleswig-Holstein, arousing popular opposition in Germany. Severe famine in Ireland: repeal of Corn Laws. First sewing machine patented (USA). Balzac: *La Cousine Bette*. |
| 1847 | In poor health, he spends summer at Winsen, where he conducts a male-voice choir. First public concert, 20 November. | Death of Mendelssohn (38). Flotow: *Martha*. Verdi: *Macbeth*. | Hamburg–America shipping line founded. Hamburg–Hanover railway. Yearly total of German emigrants to New World reaches 100,000. 'Potato Revolution' in Berlin: three days of street fighting, put down by army. Frederick William convenes United Diet: it refuses to vote money for his railway projects unless constitutional guarantees are granted. Swiss civil war won by liberal cantons, backed by Britain. First use of chloroform as an anaesthetic. Thackeray: *Vanity Fair*. |

| DATE | LIFE AND WORKS | MUSICAL CONTEXT | HISTORICAL BACKGROUND |
|------|----------------|-----------------|----------------------|
| 1848 | Hears Joachim (17) play Beethoven Violin Concerto. Spring visit to Winsen. First solo concert, 21 September. | Birth of Parry and Duparc. Death of Donizetti (51). | Revolutions throughout Europe, notably in Paris, Vienna, Prague, Berlin, Venice, Milan, Parma, Rome and Naples. Charles Albert of Piedmont invades Austrian Lombardy; defeated at Custozza. Fall of Louis Philippe: Second Republic proclaimed in France. Demonstrations throughout Germany result in appointment of liberal ministers in many states. Street fighting in Berlin brutally put down by troops; Frederick William accepts constitutional form of government and promises to lead Prussia into a united Germany. Metternich resigns and flees Vienna. An Austrian Reichstag elected; drafts new constitution. 'Vorparlament' convened in Frankfurt; a German National Assembly elected. By the end of 1848 Frederick William regains control in Berlin, granting a Prussian constitution. In Austria Schwarzenberg appointed prime minister; engineers abdication of Emperor Ferdinand in favour of his nephew Francis Joseph. First Pan–Slav Congress in Prague. Prussian occupation of Schleswig-Holstein. Communist Manifesto published. |
| 1849 | Gives second solo concert, at which he plays Beethoven's 'Waldstein' Sonata and his own 'Fantasia upon a Favourite Waltz'. Begins teaching piano and writes pot-boilers for Cranz under the name of G.W. Marks. | Death of Chopin (39). Liszt: *Tasso; Totentanz.* Meyerbeer: *Le Prophète.* Nicolai: *The Merry Wives of Windsor.* Schumann: *Manfred* completed. Verdi: *Luisa Miller.* | Frankfurt National Assembly drafts constitution of new German empire, ignoring Schwarzenberg's demands that the Habsburg empire be included. Imperial crown offered to Frederick William of Prussia who refuses it. Austrian and Prussian delegates recalled: the Assembly forcibly disbanded. Popular risings put down throughout Germany. Schwarzenberg dissolves Austrian Reichstag. Abdication of Charles Albert of Piedmont after a second unsuccessful invasion of Lombardy: succession of Victor Emmanuel. Defeat of Venetian and Roman republics. Kossuth declares a Hungarian republic. Fizeau measures the speed of light. Amelia Bloomer sets out to revolutionize women's dress. |
| 1850 | Meets Reményi. Composes (and later destroys) *Souvenir de la Russie.* Sends scores to Schumann, who returns them unopened. | Birth of Henschel and Scharwenka. Liszt completes his first 'symphonic poem'. Schumann: 'Rhenish' Symphony; *Genoveva.* Wagner: *Lohengrin.* Formation of the Bach-Gesellschaft. | Frederick William takes oath to new Prussian constitution; liberal concessions granted but the monarchy retains hold on its absolutist tools – army, bureaucracy and ruling Junker class. At Olmütz Austria, backed by Russia, puts pressure on Prussia to abandon idea of German unity. Austria defeats Hungarian revolution with Russian assistance. Austro-Hungarian inter-state customs abolished. Treaty of Berlin: Schleswig-Holstein question temporarily settled. |
| 1851 | Composes E flat minor Scherzo (op. 4), which he plays to the composer Henri Litolff; also songs and some chamber music (later destroyed). | Birth of d'Indy. Gounod: *Sappho.* Verdi: *Rigoletto.* Liszt begins issuing his Hungarian Rhapsodies. | Return to old German Confederation under Prussian and Austrian leadership; Federal Diet reconvened in Frankfurt. Bismarck Prussian minister in Frankfurt (to 1859). New Year's Patent: official re-establishment of absolutism |

| DATE | LIFE AND WORKS | MUSICAL CONTEXT | HISTORICAL BACKGROUND |
|------|----------------|-----------------|------------------------|
| 1851 cont. | | | throughout Austrian empire. Death of Ernst August of Hanover: succeeded by George V (to 1866). Louis Napoleon's *coup d'état*. Great Exhibition in London. First steel gun cast by Krupp ('the Cannon King'). Heine: *Romanzero*. Melville: *Moby-Dick*. |
| 1852 | Composes F sharp minor Piano Sonata (op. 2), and more songs. | Birth of Stanford. Schumann: *Manfred* first performed at Weimar. | Federal Diet, on a joint Austrian–Prussian motion, establishes 'reaction commission' to remove liberal ideas from all German state constitutions; free cities such as Hamburg escape the worst effects. Economic boom in Germany and Austria (to 1856). Revision of criminal law code in Austrian empire; Count Thun begins reform of education; death of Schwarzenberg; Alexander Bach assumes control. Second Empire under Napoleon III proclaimed in France. Beecher Stowe: *Uncle Tom's Cabin*. |
| 1853 | Composes C major Piano Sonata (op. 1). Concert tour with Reményi; meets Joachim in Hanover and Liszt in Weimar. Spends summer with Joachim in Göttingen; walking tour of Rhineland in September; meets the Schumanns in Düsseldorf, and Schumann's composition pupil Albert Dietrich. Schumann hails Brahms as messiah in *Neue Zeitschrift für Musik*. F-A-E Scherzo; publishes opp. 1, 3 and 6. Christmas in Hamburg. | Liszt: B minor Piano Sonata. Schumann: Violin Concerto. Verdi: *Il Trovatore; La Traviata*. Wagner completes text for *Der Ring des Nibelungen*. Steinway founds piano business in New York. | Crimean War (to 1856). Prussian law forbids labour of children under 12 and imposes strict rules on juvenile employment generally. Rising in Milan crushed. Haussmann begins reconstruction of Paris. German family magazine, *Die Gartenlaube*, founded in Leipzig. Heine: *Neueste Gedichte*. Dickens: *Bleak House*. |
| 1854 | Meets Hans von Bülow. Opp. 2, 4 and 5 published. Composes B major Trio (op. 8), 'Schumann' Variations, op. 10 Ballades; begins work on a symphony in D minor. Schumann attempts suicide and is confined in Endenich Asylum. Brahms goes to Düsseldorf to help Clara, and visits Hamburg with her in December. | Birth of Humperdinck and Janáček. Berlioz: *L'Enfance du Christ*. Liszt: 'Faust' Symphony; *Les Préludes*. | Frederick William IV achieves conversion of first chamber to a House of Lords (thus controlled by agrarian nobility) with a power of veto over all Prussian legislation. Renewal and extension of the Zollverein, including Hanover, but with Hamburg and the Hanseatic cities remaining outside. Emperor Francis Joseph marries Elisabeth of Bavaria. Completion of complex legislation giving full emancipation to peasants in the Austrian empire (one of the few measures in the 1848 constitution subsequently adhered to). Semmering railway (Austria), the first to pass through mountainous territory. Pius IX declares dogma of Immaculate Conception. *Le Figaro* begins publication in Paris. |
| 1855 | Lives in Düsseldorf. Concert tours with Clara and Joachim. B major Trio premièred in New York. | Birth of Chausson and Liadov. Berlioz: Te Deum. Verdi: *Les Vêpres Siciliennes*. | Austrian Concordat with Pope gives clergy control of education, censorship and matrimonial law. George V of Hanover abolishes liberal institutions at demand of Federal Diet. Nicholas I of Russia succeeded by Alexander II. Palmerston becomes British prime minister. Livingstone discovers Victoria Falls. Bunsen Burner invented. Burckhardt: *Cicerone*. |

| DATE | LIFE AND WORKS | MUSICAL CONTEXT | HISTORICAL BACKGROUND |
|---|---|---|---|
| 1856 | Gives more concerts. Meets Rubinstein. Begins counterpoint correspondence with Joachim. Moves to Bonn to be near Schumann. Works on op. 21 Variations and organ pieces (later destroyed). Unfinished D minor Symphony becomes first Piano Concerto. Subscribes to Bach-Gesellschaft Edition. Meets Julius Stockhausen and gives concert with him. On Schumann's death, moves to Düsseldorf to support Clara. Holiday in Switzerland marks turning point in his relations with Clara. Returns to Hamburg in October, then visits Detmold. | Birth of Sinding. Death of Schumann (46). Liszt: 'Dante' Symphony. Wagner: Full score of *Die Walküre* completed. Bechstein piano factory opened. | Austrian amnesty for Hungarian rebels of 1848. Bessemer's process for making steel. Neanderthal skull found in cave near Düsseldorf. Burton and Speke discover Lake Tanganyika. Second Opium War (to 1860). Helmholtz publishes key research on optics. Gas fires first marketed for domestic heating. Flaubert: *Madame Bovary*. |
| 1857 | Composes and teaches in Hamburg. Second visit to Detmold leads to court appointment, conducting and playing the piano. | Birth of Elgar. Death of Czerny (66) and Glinka (53). Verdi: *Simon Boccanegra*. Hans von Bülow marries Liszt's daughter Cosima. Hallé Orchestra founded in England. | World economic crisis. Indian Mutiny. Irish Republican Brotherhood (Fenians) founded in New York. Viennese inner ramparts razed: construction of Ringstrasse begins, one of most important urban planning achievements of the century. Invention of passenger lift. Baudelaire: *Les Fleurs du mal*. |
| 1858 | Works on Piano Concerto and Nonet in Hamburg. Spends summer with Clara and Joachim in Göttingen. Makes many folk-song settings and composes first Hungarian Dances; Nonet rescored as Serenade no. 1; Piano Concerto rehearsed at Hanover. Falls in love with Agathe von Siebold. | Birth of Leoncavallo, Puccini and Ethel Smyth. Berlioz: *Les Troyens* completed. Offenbach: *Orphée aux enfers*. Wagner: *Wesendonck Lieder*. Chrysander founds the Handel-Gesellschaft Edition (to which Brahms subscribes). New York Symphony Orchestra founded. | Regency of Frederick William IV's brother William after the former suffers a stroke. Dismissal of Otto von Mantueffel (prime minister since 1850); replaced by Hohenzollern and ministry of vaguely liberal bent. Marriage of Princess Victoria of England to Crown Prince Frederick William of Prussia. A unified silver currency (guilder) introduced in Austrian empire – culmination of a series of financial reforms in the 1850s including unification of taxation system and introduction for the first time of a general income tax. First transatlantic telegram. Wilhelm Busch: *Max und Moritz*. |
| 1859 | Breaks off engagement with Agathe von Siebold. First Piano Concerto premièred in Hanover, Hamburg and (disastrously) in Leipzig; First Serenade premièred in Hamburg. Founds and conducts the Hamburg Ladies' Choir, for whom he writes *Marienlieder* and Psalm 13. Second Serenade composed in last season at Detmold. | Death of Spohr (75). D. D. Emmett: *Dixie*. Gounod: *Faust*. Verdi: *Un ballo in maschera*. | Cavour, prime minister of Piedmont, enlists French aid to expel Austrians from Italy. Austrian armies defeated at Magenta and Solferino. Austria loses all her Italian possessions except Venice (Peace of Villafranca). Bismarck Prussian ambassador in St Petersburg (to 1862). Formation of German National Association by Rudolf von Bennigsen to work for German national unity under Prussia. First domestic electric lighting (USA). Darwin: *The Origin of Species by Natural Selection*. Mill: *On Liberty*. |

| DATE | LIFE AND WORKS | MUSICAL CONTEXT | HISTORICAL BACKGROUND |
|---|---|---|---|
| 1860 | Returns to Hamburg where he conducts the Second Serenade. Composes Part-songs, op. 17, Motets, op. 27 and B flat Sextet. With Joachim, publishes misguided manifesto against the 'New German' school of composition. Spends summer in Bonn with Joachim. Meets Fritz Simrock, who is to become his publisher. | Birth of Albéniz, Mahler, Wolf, Charpentier and Paderewski. Suppé composes first of all Viennese operettas, *Das Pensionat*. | Hamburg's constitution promulgated. General Albrecht von Roon introduces Prussian Army Bill, first step towards building up a highly trained professional army, directly under royal control: liberals fail to make a stand, and the way is paved for Prussia to develop into an absolute and militaristic state. Austria grants very limited constitutional government (October Diploma): an Imperial Council (Reichsrat), part appointed by the emperor, part elected by the diets, to 'collaborate' on legislation. First Italian parliament meets in Turin. Garibaldi and 'Redshirts' take Palermo and Naples. Lincoln elected president of USA. Burckhardt: *Die Kultur der Renaissance in Italien.* |
| 1861 | Lives, composes and performs in Hamburg. Works on Piano Quartet and the 'Handel' Variations, which are performed by both Brahms and Clara. | Birth of Arensky, Chaminade and MacDowell. Wagner's *Tannhäuser* causes scandal in Paris. | Austrian consitution centralized by the February Patent, unpopular with non-German nationalities. Archduke Rainier becomes prime minister, in partnership with Schmerling. Vienna granted self-government through a freely elected city council. Hungarian Diet reconvened: demands restitution of 1848 constitution and is dissolved. William I becomes Prussian king. New kingdom of Italy established with Victor Emmanuel as king. Emancipation of serfs in Russia. American Civil War (to 1865). Pneumatic drill invented. |
| 1862 | Works on *Magelone-Lieder* and String Quintet; begins Symphony in C minor. Visits Vienna for the first time; remains there through the winter, giving concerts and making new friends, including the music critic Eduard Hanslick, the composer and musicologist Gustav Nottebohm and the pianist-composer Karl Tausig. Passed over for conductorship of the Hamburg Philharmonic, which goes to his friend Stockhausen. | Birth of Debussy and Delius. Berlioz: *Béatrice et Bénédict.* Verdi: *La forza del destino.* Ludwig Köchel publishes first systematic catalogue of Mozart's works. | Liberal majority in Prussian parliament turns down government requests for army finance; king threatens to abdicate; Bismarck becomes prime minister and proceeds to raise taxes without parliamentary approval; his 'iron and blood' speech. Free trade treaty between Prussia and France. Joint Austro–German commercial code promulgated. French capture Mexico City and declare Archduke Maximilian of Austria emperor. First ocean-going steel ship, *SS Banshee*. Hugo: *Les Misérables*. Turgenev: *Fathers and Sons*. |
| 1863 | Returns to Hamburg in spring, where he composes most of his cantata *Rinaldo*. Relations between his parents deteriorating. Appointed conductor of the Vienna Singakademie; first concert features Bach, Schumann, Isaac and Beethoven. Joachim marries the contralto Amalie Weiss. | Birth of Mascagni. Berlioz: *Les Troyens à Carthage.* Bizet: *Les Pêcheurs de Perles.* | Bismarck blocks Austria's attempts to discuss a common code for trial procedure and criminal law. General German Workers' Association founded in Leipzig by Ferdinand Lassalle. Polish revolt suppressed by Russia and Prussia. Denmark again claims sovereignty over Schleswig–Holstein. May Laws in Austria establish secular jurisdiction in marriage questions, the principle of secular control of education and of equality between denominations. Lincoln issues Emancipation Proclamation, declaring all American slaves free. |

| DATE | LIFE AND WORKS | MUSICAL CONTEXT | HISTORICAL BACKGROUND |
|------|----------------|-----------------|----------------------|
| 1864 | Conducts Bach's Christmas Oratorio in Vienna. Meets Wagner (to whom he plays his 'Handel' Variations). Forced to accept that his parents should separate, he visits Hamburg to make the necessary arrangements, and contributes to the financial support of both households despite his modest means. Resigns from Singakademie in spring; spends summer at Lichtenthal with Clara. Based in Vienna during winter; meets the conductor Hermann Levi, and the novelist Ivan Turgenev. | Birth of Richard Strauss. Death of Meyerbeer (73). Bruckner: Mass in D minor. Offenbach: *La Belle Hélène*. Rossini: *Petite Messe solennelle*. | Prussian and Austrian troops invade Schleswig-Holstein. Pope Pius IX issues encyclical denouncing liberalism. First Socialist International (Karl Marx as Secretary). Viennese Museum für Kunst und Industrie opens (modelled on the Victoria and Albert Museum in London). Ludwig II becomes king of Bavaria. Red Cross founded. *Neue Freie Presse* established in Vienna. |
| 1865 | Mother dies. Works on German Requiem in Vienna. Spends summer in Lichtenthal; writes Horn Trio. Concert tours in autumn; premières 'Paganini' Variations in Zürich. | Birth of Dukas, Glazunov, Nielsen and Sibelius. Liszt: *Missa Choralis*. Meyerbeer: *L'Africaine*. Wagner: *Tristan und Isolde*. Schubert's 'Unfinished' Symphony premièred in Vienna, 43 years after its composition. | Resignation of Rainer–Schmerling cabinet: constitution of 1860–1 suspended. Belcredi prime minister (to 1867). Hungarian Diet reopened; emperor recognizes validity of 1848 constitution. Prusso-German customs union renewed. Partition of Schleswig-Holstein between Prussia and Austria (Gastein Convention). Bismarck meets Napoleon at Biarritz. Ringstrasse opens in Vienna. Assassination of President Lincoln in the US. Mendel enunciates Law of Heredity. Whymper climbs the Matterhorn. |
| 1866 | Brahms festival at Oldenburg organized by Dietrich, now Kapellmeister to the Grand Duke. Visits Switzerland with Joachim. Meets the famous surgeon Theodor Billroth who becomes one of his closest friends. More work on Requiem; completes G major Sextet. Spends autumn in Vienna and Christmas at Oldenburg. Brahms's father marries Caroline Schnack, a widow 20 years his junior. | Birth of Busoni and Satie. Bruckner: Symphony no. 1. Offenbach: *La Vie Parisienne*. Smetana: *The Bartered Bride*. Tchaikovsky: Symphony no. 1. | Prusso-Italian alliance; Franco-Austrian alliance. Bismarck presents Frankfurt Diet with plan for the formation of a new German constitution excluding Austria. War breaks out, with German states split in their support for Prussia and Austria. Prussia defeats pro-Austrian Hanover; king escapes abroad. Italian invasion of Venetia; Austrians defeat Italians at Custozza. Prussians defeat Austrians at Sadowka. French mediate peace settlement. Venice ceded to Italy. Bismarck proposes a North German Confederation under Prussian leadership; Prussian population augmented by 4 million after annexation of defeated states – Hanover, Hesse-Kassel, Nassau and Frankfurt, and later Schleswig-Holstein. Austria's ally, Saxony, retains independence. Bismarck concludes treaties with south German states whose armies are put at Prussia's disposal in time of war. Conservatives successful in Prussian elections; liberal parties regroup. Larousse: *Grand dictionnaire universel*. Dostoevsky: *Crime and Punishment*. |

| DATE | LIFE AND WORKS | MUSICAL CONTEXT | HISTORICAL BACKGROUND |
|------|---------------|-----------------|------------------------|
| 1867 | Concert tours of Austria in the spring and autumn (the latter with Joachim); summer walking tour with father in Austrian Alps. Three movements of the German Requiem performed (unsuccessfully) in Vienna. | Birth of Granados, Koechlin and Toscanini. Gounod: *Roméo et Juliette*. Johann Strauss II: 'Blue Danube' Waltz. Verdi: *Don Carlos*. | North German Reichstag, dominated by Prussian delegates, passes Bismarck's draft constitution. A German customs parliament set up. Belcredi succeeded by Beust, then by Karl Auersperg, as Austrian prime minister. Austro-Hungarian compromise (Ausgleich) establishes Dual Monarchy, opposed by nine other nationalities in the empire, particulary the Czechs. Count Andrássy becomes Hungarian prime minister (to 1871). Austrian government wins support for Ausgleich in Vienna by granting constitutional reforms (December). Emperor Maximilian (Francis Joseph's brother) executed in Mexico. Bismarck thwarts Napoleon III's attempts to gain control of Luxembourg. Francis Joseph and Napoleon III meet at Salzburg. Second Pan–Slav Congress held in Moscow. Garibaldi marches on Rome: defeated by French and papal troops. Werner von Siemens invents dynamo. First bicycles manufactured (in France). Bauernfeld: *Aus der Gesellschaft*. Marx: *Das Kapital* (vol. 1). |
| 1868 | German Requiem premièred in Bremen Cathedral. *Schicksalslied* begun. Concert tours in Germany and Denmark with Stockhausen; concerts in the autumn with Clara and Stockhausen. | Death of Rossini (76). Boito: *Mefistofele*. Grieg: Piano Concerto in A minor. Wagner: *Die Meistersinger von Nürnberg*. | Bismarck introduces industrial freedom by decree; further legislation 1868–70 promotes commercial and legal integration (including a North German code of criminal law in 1870) of states within confederation, facilitating economic development. A modicum of self-administration is granted to the annexed territories, but Prussian tax, law and military systems universally applied. Removal of government obstacles to marriage and declaration of equality of all religions. Gladstone prime minister in Britain (to 1874). Hamburg Kunsthalle founded by Alfred Lichtwark. Ernst Haeckel: *History of Natural Creation*. |
| 1869 | Cantata *Rinaldo* premièred in Vienna; final version of Requiem in Leipzig. Composes Alto Rhapsody and *Liebeslieder* Waltzes; publishes Hungarian Dances. Engagement of Julie Schumann. Tour to Budapest with Stockhausen. Settles permanently in Vienna in the autumn. | Birth of Roussel and Pfitzner. Death of Berlioz (66). Bruch: Violin Concerto no. 1. Bruckner: Mass in F minor. Wagner: *Das Rheingold*. Opening of Vienna Hofoper. | German Social Democratic Workers' Party founded under August Bebel. In Austria industrial workers gain (restricted) right to form trade unions and (1870) to strike. Law on elementary and public education in Austria sets secular structure of grade and public schools. Administration of Galicia handed over to Polish majority. Hungarian–Croation Law of Compromise. Theophilus Hansen's new Musikverein completed; artist Hans Makart brought to Vienna to contribute decorative schemes for Ringstrasse buildings. Postcards introduced to Austria, to Brahms's delight. Opening of Suez Canal. Tolstoy: *War and Peace* completed. |

| DATE | LIFE AND WORKS | MUSICAL CONTEXT | HISTORICAL BACKGROUND |
|---|---|---|---|
| 1870 | Alto Rhapsody premièred in Jena. No new works completed. Attends performances of Wagner's *Das Rheingold* and *Die Walküre* in Munich. | Delibes: *Coppélia*. Tchaikovsky: *Romeo and Juliet*. Wagner marries Cosima von Bülow. Founding of Société Nationale de Musique in France. | Franco-Prussian war. Prussia supported by south German states as per treaty; Austria-Hungary remains neutral. French defeated at Sedan. Fall of Louis Napoleon; Republicans reject peace settlement; siege of Paris. Bismarck concludes treaties of federation with south German states. Catholic Centre Party founded in Prussia; its leader Ludwig Windthorst becomes one of Bismarck's most formidable opponents. Vatican Council announce dogma of papal infallibility. French expelled from Rome: Rome becomes Italian capital. Austrian Concordat of 1855 terminated. Schliemann begins excavation of Troy. |
| 1871 | *Schicksalslied* premièred in Karlsruhe; first part of *Triumphlied* performed in Bremen in memory of war dead. Begins teaching Florence May. Moves to 4 Karlgasse in Vienna, his permanent home. | Verdi: *Aida*. Royal Albert Hall opened in London. *L'Internationale* composed in France. | French provisional government formed under Thiers. Alsace, Strasbourg, Metz and part of Lorraine ceded to Germany, causing great resentment. King William of Prussia accepts the title of German emperor. German mark replaces 33 state currencies. Burst of economic expansion in Germany (to 1873). Beginning of Bismarck's anti-clerical *Kulturkampf*. Austrian prime minister Count Hohenwart's attempt to reach settlement with the Czechs fails due to Hungarian opposition to federalization of the empire. Split in Czech National Party, with progressive 'Young Czech' wing gaining in popularity. Adolf Auersperg Austrian prime minister (to 1879); liberal adminstration characterized by internal dissent and vociferous Slav federalist opposition. |
| 1872 | Father dies. *Triumphlied* given complete. Summer in Baden; meets Nietzsche. Becomes director of Gesellschaft der Musikfreunde, succeeding Anton Rubinstein – gives six concerts per season for the next three years. | Birth of Scriabin and Vaughan Williams. Bizet: *L'Arlésienne*. Bruckner: Symphony no. 2. | Abolition of church supervision of schools in Prussia. Jesuit order suppressed in Germany. German *Kräsordnung* reorganizes administration of rural counties – a landmark in the demise of feudalism. Three Emperors' League (Germany, Austria-Hungary, Russia) formed in Berlin. Death of Austrian dramatist Franz Grillparzer: his last three plays (*Die Jüdin von Toledo*, *Ein Bruderzwist in Habsburg* and *Libussa*) first published and performed in Vienna 1872–4. New Viennese Stadttheater founded with Heinrich Laube as director. Eliot: *Middlemarch*. Turgenev: *A Month in the Country*. |
| 1873 | Completes first two string quartets and 'Haydn' Variations. Attends Schumann festival in Bonn, organized by Joachim; visits World Exhibition in Vienna. | Birth of Rachmaninov, Reger, Caruso and Chaliapin. Bruckner: Symphony no. 3. Tchaikovsky: Symphony no. 2. | May Laws in Prussia: state control over church appointments to be enforced; papal jurisdiction over Catholic Church abolished. German forces withdraw from France on full payment of war indemnity. Stock Exchange crash in Vienna (May); similar crash in Germany (October) followed by depression lasting, apart from a few brief upsurges, until 1895. Direct elections to parliament for the first time in Austria, though |

| DATE | LIFE AND WORKS | MUSICAL CONTEXT | HISTORICAL BACKGROUND |
|---|---|---|---|
| 1873 cont. | | | franchise still limited by strict property qualifications. New code of criminal procedure (Austria) introduces trial by jury (with many qualifications). Opening of Viennese World Exhibition. Eduard Suess develops Vienna's water supply system, pumping water from the Alps. First mass production of typewriters (USA). |
| 1874 | Completes C minor Piano Quartet. Meets the Herzogenbergs and Bach biographer Philipp Spitta in Leipzig where the Gewandhaus stages a 'Brahms week'. Later meets singer and composer Georg Henschel. Friendship develops with Joseph Widmann, Swiss poet and playwright, during summer spent near Zürich. Ludwig II of Bavaria awards Brahms the Order of Maximilian (to Wagner's annoyance). | Birth of Schoenberg, Holst and Ives. Bruckner: Symphony no. 4. Mussorgsky: *Boris Godunov*. Smetana: *Vltava*. Johann Strauss II: *Die Fledermaus*. Verdi: *Requiem*. | Bismarck gets German parliament to agree to a septennial voting of military budget. Obligatory civil marriage law (Prussia: applied to empire 1875). In spite of Bismarck's efforts, Catholic Centre Party doubles its vote and becomes second largest party in German parliament, maintaining its hold for next 60 years. New set of May Laws in Austria further weakens powers of Roman Catholic Church. Disraeli prime minister in Britain (to 1880). First Impressionist exhibition in Paris. Verlaine: *Romances sans paroles*. |
| 1875 | Resigns as director of Gesellschaft. Continues work on First Symphony. First championing of Dvořák; estrangement from Levi. | Birth of Ravel. Death of Bizet (36), not long after disastrous première of *Carmen*. Gilbert and Sullivan: *Trial by Jury*. Tchaikovsky: Piano Concerto no. 1. | Central Bank (Reichsbank) founded in Germany. The *Provinzialordnung* allows individual German states self-government in such limited areas as highways and social welfare. Nationalist Kálmán Tisza prime minister in Hungary (to 1890). Revolt against Turkish rule in Bosnia. Twain: *The Adventures of Tom Sawyer*. |
| 1876 | Completes First Symphony (premièred in Karlsruhe under Otto Dessoff) and Third String Quartet. Visits Holland, Mannheim and Koblenz; conducts First Symphony in Mannheim and Munich. Summer holiday with Henschel on the Baltic island of Rügen. | Birth of Falla, Ruggles, Casals and Bruno Walter. Ponchielli: *Gioconda*. Tchaikovsky: *Swan Lake*. Opening of Festspielhaus at Bayreuth with first complete performance of Wagner's *Ring* cycle. | Serbia and Montenegro at war with Turkey. 'Bulgarian Atrocities'. Queen Victoria becomes Empress of India. New Ottoman constitution proclaimed. Alexander Bell files first patent for the telephone. First practical carpet-sweeper. Invention of the Bentwood chair for use in cafés by Gebruder Thonet, Vienna. |
| 1877 | Declines to receive honorary degree from Cambridge University, being reluctant to make the journey to England; instead, Joachim gives British première of Symphony no. 1 in Cambridge. Shortly afterwards Brahms revises the work. Spends summer in Pörtschach and Lichtenthal; composes motet *Warum ist das Licht gegeben?* Second Symphony completed and premièred in Vienna by Hans Richter to great acclaim. | Birth of Dohnányi. Chabrier: *L'Etoile*. Saint-Saëns: *Samson et Dalila*. First publication of Mozart's complete works begun. | Russia declares war on Turkey; grants Austria-Hungary rights to Bosnia and Herzegovina. Victorious Russians conclude Treaty of San Stefano with Turks – unacceptable to other Great Powers. Law on organization of courts and codes of criminal and civil procedure promulgated throughout German empire. Move to free trade completed with lifting of last import duties (on iron): strong opposition from German industrialists and landowners. Socialists gain 12 seats in German Parliament. Hansen's Viennese Akademie der Bildenden Künste completed. Edison invents the phonograph. Tolstoy: *Anna Karenina* completed. |

| DATE | LIFE AND WORKS | MUSICAL CONTEXT | HISTORICAL BACKGROUND |
|------|----------------|-----------------|------------------------|
| 1878 | Begins works on Violin Concerto and op. 76 Piano Pieces. First Italian holiday with Billroth; summer at Pörtschach. Offered Bach's old post as Thomaskantor in Leipzig, but declines. Wolf (18) seeks and rejects Brahms's advice, becoming his lifelong enemy. | Dvořák: Slavonic Dances. Gilbert and Sullivan: *H.M.S. Pinafore.* Tchaikovsky: Violin Concerto and Symphony no. 4. George Grove publishes first volume of his mammoth *Dictionary of Music and Musicians.* | Treaty of San Stefano renegotiated in Berlin, Bismarck acting as 'honest broker': partition of Bulgaria between Russians and Turks; Austria retains Bosnia and Herzegovina; Serbia freed from Turkish control. Death of Pius IX; Bismarck relaxes *Kulturkampf* (ends 1887) to secure co-operation of Centre Party; uses two attempts on the emperor's life as an excuse to introduce Anti-Socialist Law. Invention of the microphone; first electric street lighting (in London). |
| 1879 | Violin Concerto premièred in Leipzig and repeated in Vienna; G major Violin Sonata and op. 79 Rhapsodies for piano composed. Receives honorary doctorate from Breslau University. Summer at Pörtschach; tours Hungary, Transylvania and Poland with Joachim in the autumn. Wagner attacks Brahms in 'Über das Dichten und Komponieren'. | Birth of Bridge, Ireland, Respighi and Karg-Elert. Bruckner: String Quintet. Franck: Piano Quintet. Tchaikovsky: *Eugene Onegin.* | Austro–German alliance (to 1918). A federal supreme court (Reichsgericht) established in Leipzig. Bismarck ends co-operation with liberals and launches new economic programme, reverting to protectionist trade policy. Fall of Auersperg government in Austria; conservative administration under Count Taafe lasts 14 years; Czech boycott (since 1867) of parliament lifted. First electric passenger railway demonstrated by Siemens in Berlin. Ibsen: *A Doll's House.* Treitschke: *German History in the Nineteenth Century.* |
| 1880 | Composes Academic Festival and Tragic Overtures; publishes Books 3 and 4 of Hungarian Dances. Attends unveiling of Schumann memorial in Bonn. First summer at Ischl; meets composers Johann Strauss II and Ignaz Brüll. Serious rift with Joachim when Brahms sides with Joachim's wife Amalie in divorce case. | Birth of Bloch and Medtner. Dvořák: Symphony no. 6. Gilbert and Sullivan: *The Pirates of Penzance.* Mahler: *Das klagende Lied.* Philipp Spitta publishes historic biography of J.S. Bach. | Gladstone prime minister again in Britain. First Boer War (to 1881). Game of Bingo developed from Italian 'tombola'. Electric light bulbs manufactured. Advent of tinned foods. Artist Max Klinger dedicates his cycle *Amor and Psyche* to Brahms. First photogravures published by Klič, Vienna. Maupassant: *Boule de suif.* Dostoevsky: *The Brothers Karamazov.* |
| 1881 | Academic Festival Overture premièred at Breslau. Completes Second Piano Concerto (which he premières in Budapest) and the cantata *Nänie*. Tours Holland and Hungary, renewing his acquaintance with Liszt. Spring holiday in Italy and Sicily with Billroth and Nottebohm; spends summer at Pressbaum. | Birth of Bartók, Enescu and Miaskovsky. Death of Mussorgsky (42). Bruckner: Symphony no. 6. Fauré: Ballade. Offenbach: *Les Contes d'Hoffmann.* | Three Emperors' Alliance. Assassination of Tsar Alexander II. Austro–Hungarian alliance with Serbia. First blast-furnace in Germany employing Gilchrist method: by 1900 German iron ore output almost equals and steel output surpasses that of Britain. Rapid development of German shipbuilding industry begins. First electric tram in operation (Berlin). *Chat noir*, first of all cabarets, founded in Paris. James: *The Portrait of a Lady.* |
| 1882 | Completes C major Piano Trio, F major String Quintet and *Gesang der Parzen*. Introduces Second Piano Concerto in many German and Dutch cities. Summer in Ischl. Holiday in Italy with Billroth, Simrock and Brüll. With Nottebohm when he dies at Graz. | Birth of Grainger, Kodály, Stravinsky, Szymanowski. Tchaikovsky: 1812 Overture. Wagner: *Parsifal.* Berlin Philharmonic founded. | Triple Alliance of Austria–Hungary, Germany and Italy. Linz Programme advocating union of all German-speaking Austrian lands. Hague Convention fixes three-mile limit for territorial waters. Camera film first manufactured. |

| DATE | LIFE AND WORKS | MUSICAL CONTEXT | HISTORICAL BACKGROUND |
|---|---|---|---|
| 1883 | Completes Third Symphony, which is premièred in Vienna under Richter. Forms a close relationship with Hermine Spies during summer spent at Wiesbaden. | Birth of Bax and Varèse. Death of Wagner (69). Bruckner: Symphony no. 7. Delibes: *Lakmé*. | Bismarck initiates programme of social legislation, beginning with health insurance. Taafe begins a similar programme in Austria (to 1889). Construction of Rathaus in Vienna (designed by Friedrich von Schmidt) and of Hansen's parliament building completed. First skyscraper, Chicago. |
| 1884 | Begins Fouth Symphony. Spring in Italy; summer at Mürzzuschlag with Hanslick. Forms close friendship with Fellinger family in Vienna. Winter tour with Hermine Spies. | Death of Smetana (60). Bruckner: Te Deum. Mahler: *Lieder eines fahrenden Gesellen*. Massenet: *Manon*. Puccini: *Le Villi*. Spitta begins work on complete edition of Schütz. | Berlin conference of 14 nations on African affairs. Bismarck declares South-West Africa a German protectorate. Accident insurance introduced in Germany. Vienna University building (designed by Heinrich von Ferstel) completed. First Oxford English Dictionary published. Ibsen: *The Wild Duck*. Twain: *Huckleberry Finn*. |
| 1885 | Completes Fourth Symphony; conducts première at Meiningen, where he meets Richard Strauss. Rift with Bülow. | Birth of Berg. Dvořák: Symphony no. 7. Franck: *Variations symphoniques*. Gilbert and Sullivan: *The Mikado*. Liszt: *Bagatelle Without Tonality*. Johann Strauss II: *Der Zigeunerbaron*. | Germany annexes Tanganyika and Zanzibar and founds colonies in north-eastern New Guinea. Popular uprisings in Bulgaria lead to virtual unification under Russian Prince Alexander Battenberg (deposed 1886). Benz builds single-cylinder engine for motor car. Individuality of fingerprints established. Pasteur uses inoculation to cure a child with rabies. Zola: *Germinal.* |
| 1886 | Spends summer at Hofstetten, near Thun in Switzerland, where he composes Cello Sonata no. 2 in F, Violin Sonata no. 2 in A and Piano Trio no. 3 in C minor. Elected honorary president of the Vienna Tonkünstlerverein. | Birth of Furtwängler. Death of Liszt (74) and Ponchielli (51). Fauré: Requiem. Franck: Violin Sonata. Mussorgsky (completed Rimsky-Korsakov): *Khovanshchina*. Invention of the celeste. | 30,000 Poles expelled from Prussia; government start to buy up estates of Polish nobility. Death of Ludwig II of Bavaria. Gladstone defeated over Irish Home Rule Bill. Bonaparte and Orléans families banished from France. Ernst Mach's *Contribution to the Analysis of the Sensations.* Rimbaud: *Les Illuminations.* Stevenson: *Dr Jekyll and Mr Hyde.* |
| 1887 | Composes Double Concerto and *Zigeunerlieder* at Thun; première of Double Concerto marks reconciliation with Joachim. Holiday in Italy with Simrock and pianist-composer Theodor Kirchner. | Birth of Villa-Lobos. Death of Borodin (53). Bruckner: Symphony no. 8. Chabrier: *Le Roi malgré lui*. Gilbert and Sullivan: *Ruddigore*. Goldmark: *Rustic Wedding*. Richard Strauss: *Aus Italien*. Verdi: *Otello*. | Bulgarians elect Austrian candidate, Prince Ferdinand of Coburg, as their ruler. Triple Alliance renewed. Prussia and Russia sign 'Reinsurance Treaty'. Telephone introduced to general usage in Austria. Queen Victoria's Golden Jubilee in Britain. 'Bloody Sunday' in London. Hertz demonstrates radio waves. Berliner patents the gramophone. Zamenhof devises 'Esperanto'. Strindberg: *The Father.* Conan Doyle writes first Sherlock Holmes story ('A Study in Scarlet'). |
| 1888 | Composes Third Violin Sonata at Thun. Meets Grieg (whom he likes) and Tchaikovsky (whom he doesn't). Spring in Italy with Widmann; meets pianist and conductor Giuseppe Martucci in Bologna. | Birth of Irving Berlin. Death of Marxsen (81). Debussy finishes *La Damoiselle élue*. Franck: Symphony in D minor. Rimsky-Korsakov: *Sheherazade*. Satie: *Gymnopédies*. Tchaikovksy: Symphony no. 5. | Death of Emperor William I, aged 91, and of his successor Frederick III, whose son becomes William II. Hamburg and Bremen finally join customs union with German empire. First draft of codification of German civil law presented: process completed 1900. Aeronautical exhibition in Vienna; Semper and Hansenauer's new Burgtheater completed. Eastman perfects box camera. Dunlop invents pneumatic tyre. Strindberg: *Miss Julie.* |

| DATE | LIFE AND WORKS | MUSICAL CONTEXT | HISTORICAL BACKGROUND |
|------|----------------|-----------------|------------------------|
| 1889 | Composes *Fest- und Gedenksprüche* and Motets, op. 110; radically revises Piano Trio, op. 8. Order of Leopold conferred on him by Emperor Franz Joseph; awarded the freedom of the city of Hamburg. Summer at Ischl. | Dvořák: Symphony no. 8. Gilbert and Sullivan: *The Gondoliers.* Mahler: Symphony no. 1. Richard Strauss: *Don Juan.* | Suicide of Crown Prince Rudolf (Austria–Hungary) at Mayerling. Austrian Social Democratic Party formed at Hainfeld. Disability and old age insurance introduced in Germany. General strike of miners in the Ruhr (William II intervenes in their support). Second International in Paris. Punched-card machine patented (US). Hauptmann: *Vor Sonnenaufgang.* Gide begins his journal. |
| 1890 | Composes Second String Quintet. Spring holiday in Italy with Widmann; summer at Ischl. Meets Alice Barbi. | Birth of Ibert and Frank Martin. Death of Franck (67). Borodin: *Prince Igor.* Mascagni: *Cavalleria rusticana.* Richard Strauss: *Tod und Verklärung.* Tchaikovsky: *The Queen of Spades.* Wolf: *Spanisches Liederbuch.* | Social Democrat vote doubles in German election, winning them 35 seats. William II refuses to sanction Bismarck's repressive policies; he is forced to resign and replaced by General Leo von Caprivi. Anti-Socialist legislation in Germany expires. Anglo-German treaty seeks to resolve colonial conflicts. Development of the electrical industry in Germany during the 1890s. First entirely steel-framed building erected in Chicago. First orchestral recordings released. |
| 1891 | Composes Clarinet Trio and Clarinet Quintet, inspired by the playing of Richard Mühlfeld. Makes will ('Ischl testament'). | Birth of Prokofiev. Death of Delibes (55). Fauré: *La Bonne Chanson.* Rachmaninov completes Piano Concerto no. 1. Wolf: *Italienisches Liederbuch.* | William II abolishes Sunday working and limits working hours of women and children. Triple Alliance of Germany, Austria and Italy renewed for 12 years. German Social Democratic Party adopts Marxist ideology. Works starts on Trans-Siberian railway. |
| 1892 | Begins composing final sequence of piano pieces (opp. 116–19). Deaths of Elisabeth von Herzogenberg and of his sister Elise leave Brahms desolate. Spends spring in Italy, and summer in Ischl. | Birth of Honegger and Milhaud. Catalani: *La Wally.* Dvořák: Te Deum. Leoncavallo: *Pagliacci* Massenet: *Werther.* Nielsen: Symphony no. 1. Rachmaninov: Prelude in C sharp minor. Sibelius: *Kullervo.* | Devastating cholera epidemic in Hamburg. Newly built Kunsthistorisches Museum opens in Vienna. Germany and Britain agree over the Cameroons. Diesel patents his internal combustion engine. First automatic telephone switchboard (USA). Hauptmann: *Die Weber.* Nietzsche: *Also sprach Zarathustra.* Ibsen: *The Master Builder.* Maeterlinck: *Pelléas et Mélisande.* |
| 1893 | Holiday in Italy and Sicily with Widmann to avoid 60th birthday celebrations. Working on Piano Pieces, op. 118–19 at Ischl during summer. Death of Hermine Spies. | Birth of Cole Porter. Death of Tchaikovsky (53) and Gounod (75). Debussy: String Quartet. Dvořák: Symphony no. 9, 'From the New World'. Humperdinck: *Hänsel und Gretel.* Puccini: *Manon Lescaut.* Sibelius: *Karelia Suite.* Tchaikovksy: Symphony no. 6. Verdi: *Falstaff.* | Franco-Russian alliance. Germany begins tariff war against Russia. An army bill increases size of German army but reduces military service to two years. Windischgrätz becomes Austrian prime minister (to 1895). Riots in Prague over Taafe's division of administration on the lines of nationality. Taafe's suffrage bill defeated. Vienna Linienwall dismantled and a second ringroad, the Gürtel, constructed. Independent Labour Party founded in Britain. Art Nouveau appears in Europe. |

| DATE | LIFE AND WORKS | MUSICAL CONTEXT | HISTORICAL BACKGROUND |
|---|---|---|---|
| 1894 | Further bereavement with deaths of Billroth, Bülow and Spitta. Summer at Ischl; composes the two Clarinet Sonatas. Publishes the 49 *Deutsche Volkslieder*. Declines conductorship of Hamburg Philharmonic. Accompanies Alice Barbi at farewell recital. | Death of Chabrier (53) and Rubinstein (64). Debussy: *Prélude à l'après-midi d'un faune* (often cited as 'the beginning of modern music'). Massenet: *Thaïs* Richard Strauss: *Guntram*. | Social Democrats hold first mass demonstration in Vienna. Pan–German League founded. Prince Chlodwig von Hohenlohe becomes German chancellor. German–Russian commercial treaty. German landowners, angered by concessions to industry, form Agrarian League. Death of Alexander III; Nicholas II becomes tsar of Russia. Dreyfus trial in France. Sino–Japanese war (to 1895). Roseberry becomes British prime minister. Rilke: *Leben und Lieder*. Schnitzler: *Das Märchen*. |
| 1895 | Tours German cities with Mühlfeld, performing the Clarinet Sonatas. Summer at Ischl. Festival of 'the three B's' (Bach–Beethoven–Brahms) at Meiningen. Visits Clara in Frankfurt. | Birth of Hindemith and Orff. Debussy completes first version of *Pelléas et Mélisande*. Dvořák: Cello Concerto. Mahler: Symphony no. 2. Strauss: *Till Eulenspiegels lustige Streiche*. First Promenade Concerts at the Queen's Hall in London. | Austrian code of civil procedure enacted. Badeni becomes prime minister. Röntgen discovers X-rays. Marconi invents radio telegraphy. First public film shows (Berlin and Paris). First petrol-driven motorbus (Germany). Kiel Canal links Baltic and North Sea. Fontane: *Effi Briest*. Wedekind: *Erdgeist* (first 'Lulu' play). Schnitzler: *Liebelei*. Breuer and Freud: *Studien über Hysterie*. |
| 1896 | Composes *Vier ernste Gesänge*; begins work on Chorale Preludes for organ (his last work). Conducts both piano concertos in Berlin, with Eugen d'Albert as soloist. Death of Clara Schumann; undertakes 40-hour journey to attend her funeral, but arrives too late. Spends summer at Ischl; rapid deterioration in health; travels to Karlsbad to take the waters; returns to Vienna but health steadily worsens. Attends Bruckner's funeral. | Death of Bruckner (72) and Clara Schumann (77). Bruckner: Symphony no. 9 (unfinished). Elgar: *King Olaf*. Gilbert and Sullivan: *The Grand Duke* (their last operetta). Giordano: *Andrea Chenier*. Mahler: Symphony no. 3. Puccini: *La Bohème*. Richard Strauss: *Also sprach Zarathustra*. Wolf: *Der Corregidor*. First use of quarter-tones in European music (in a string quartet by Foulds). | Death of Francis Joseph's brother and heir, Charles Louis, whose son, Franz Ferdinand, becomes heir to the empire. Further electoral reforms under Badeni pave way for introduction of full male suffrage in 1907. New evidence for the innocence of Dreyfus suppressed in France. First ski school opens in Austria. Becquerel reports the discovery of radio-activity. Henry Ford builds his first car. Nobel prizes established. First modern Olympic Games held in Athens. Fontane: *Die Poggenpuhls*. Chekhov: *The Seagull*. |
| 1897 | Last appearance in public, at a performance of Fourth Symphony, under Hans Richter. Revises his will; declines rapidly and dies in Vienna from cancer of the liver on 3 April. Lavish public funeral on 6 April. | Birth of Korngold and Cowell. Rachmaninov: Symphony no. 1. Richard Strauss: *Don Quixote*. Mahler becomes conductor of the Vienna Opera. | Germany occupies Kiao-chow in northern China. Tirpitz appointed German naval secretary. Queen Victoria celebrates her Diamond Jubilee. Badeni's language ordinances provoke riots in Bohemia, leading to his dismissal. Emperor finally recognizes Christian Socialist Karl Lueger as Mayor of Vienna after he is elected for the fifth time since 1895. Founding of the Vienna Sezession by artists Gustav Klimt and Karl Moll. First Zionist conference at Basle. Rilke: *Traumgekrönt*. H.G. Wells: *The Invisible Man*. Rostand: *Cyrano de Bergerac*. Havelock Ellis: *Studies in the Psychology of Sex*. |

The publishers gratefully acknowledge permission given by the following to reproduce illustrations and photographs:

Page vi Bildarchiv Preussischer Kulturbesitz, Berlin viii Lebrecht Collection; 2 Gesellschaft der Musikfreunde, Vienna; 3 Gesellschaft der Musikfreunde, Vienna; 4 Gesellschaft der Musikfreunde, Vienna; 5 Gesellschaft der Musikfreunde, Vienna; 12 Gesellschaft der Musikfreunde, Vienna; 15 Lebrecht Collection; 20 Lebrecht Collection; 30 AKG London; 36–37 Lebrecht Collection; 39 Gesellschaft der Musikfreunde, Vienna; 42 Museum für Kunst und Kulturgeschichte, Marburg/AKG London; 51 Gesellschaft der Musikfreunde, Vienna; 54 Gesellschaft der Musikfreunde, Vienna; 59 Historisches Museum der Stadt Wien/AKG London; 62 Private Collection, Bonn/AKG London; 65 AKG London; 67 AKG London; 68 Lebrecht Collection; 72 Lebrecht Collection; 73 AKG London; 77 AKG London; 87 Lebrecht Collection; 88 Lebrecht Collection; 91 Lebrecht Collection; 93 Lebrecht Collection; 96 Gesellschaft der Musikfreunde, Vienna; 98 National Portrait Gallery, London; 105 AKG London; 108 Gesellschaft der Musikfreunde, Vienna; 111 Österreichischen Nationalbibliothek, Vienna; 114 AKG London; 116 Archiv für Kunst und Geschichte, Berlin/AKG London; 117 Archiv für Kunst und Geschichte, Berlin/AKG London; 120 Gesellschaft der Musikfreunde, Vienna; 123 Lebrecht Collection; 126 AKG London; 129 Gesellschaft der Musikfreunde, Vienna; 130 Gesellschaft der Musikfreunde, Vienna; 131 Lebrecht Collection; 134 Lebrecht Collection; 136 © RA Frieder Roth, Munich/AKG London; 141 Lebrecht Collection; 142 AKG London; 145 AKG London; 146 Lebrecht Collection; 150 Bildarchiv Preussischer Kulturbesitz, Berlin; 154 Lebrecht Collection; 155 AKG London.

Haydn

Schumann

Gluck

Handel

Bruckner

Bach

Liszt

Mozart